Sheelagh Kanelli

Sheelagh Kanelli was born and educated in England, went to Greece as an 'au pair' in the 1950s, and met and married her husband in Kalamata, where she opened a School of English. She wrote a 'semi-autobiography about Greek life', *Earth and Water*, which was published in the UK in 1965, and also in the US.

She writes that she has always been very involved in local Greek life, especially the position of women – and children – and after the fall of the Dictatorship in July 1974 helped to found a Women's Rights Movement in Kalamata.

She wrote *The Nets* during the Dictatorship of the Colonels (1967–74), after reading about the death of 21 fourteen-year-old schoolgirls who were drowned while on a school excursion to Crete in May 1971.

SHEELAGH KANELLI

The Nets

 The Women's Press

First published by The Women's Press 1983
A member of the Namara Group
124 Shoreditch High Street, London E1 6JE

British Library Cataloguing in Publication Data

Kanelli, Sheelagh
   The nets.
   I. Title
   823'.914]F[PR6061.A/

Typeset by MC Typeset, Rochester, Kent
Printed in Great Britain by Nene Litho
and bound by Woolnough Bookbinding
both of Wellingborough, Northants

For Christiana

Acknowledgements

The author is grateful for permission to quote lines from 'Agianapi I' by George Seferis, published in *Four Greek Poets*. Penguin Books, Harmondsworth, 1966; and from *Gestures* by Yannis Ritsos, translated by Nikos Stangos, published by Cape Goliard Press, London 1971.

1   The Boat

Dissolving shapes, moving: _ a feeling of
unrest, deceptive wateriness _ the sound of
water surrounds you, changing, deep,
uncontrollable; you too are uncontrollable,
almost free.
                    Yannis Ritsos: 'Dissolution' 1968

The sea, when you are ten, has, from
your height, different planes and surfaces, facets and
another horizon which adults cannot see.

Anna said: 'Look! Look at the sun shining on the
sea. It's like lighted candles!'

And the mother, the adult, said yes dear, not
seeing the candles at all.

She tugged the child's hand, pulling her away from
the sea and what she had seen there, almost afraid of
it, and wondering at what Anna had said, what she
might be, when grown up – as if the child had no
being yet. She herself had not seen the candles
although she knew they were there. Sometimes it is
better not to know, but to create instead the unreal

necessities of getting home at the right time, seeing to the meal and the house and can we afford it.

Another day, she thought, I must make more time for the child, feeling that if Anna managed to escape into the future, she herself would know freedom again. But a child cannot grasp the idea of future while an adult knows it is an illusion. It is the same with freedom. It is only that the absence of freedom is more terrible. Her husband had fallen into apathy ever since that early dawn last year when the country itself had had freedom stolen from it. She often thought it seemed frivolous, like regretting the loss of a petty privilege, to reply, when asked, that its loss had meant that her husband no longer wanted to write his book. After all, so many others suffered so many things in Greece these days. Yet this too was real. It was vital.

And so she found herself pulling the child away as though in guilt. But in Anna being pulled away, there grew a great longing for the wide sea and its far horizon. She would come back some other time, she thought, on some other holiday away from her inland home pressed round by the mountains, where there was no horizon, where she lived out her childhood, restricted by restricted people, by lessons and the endless ticking of the clock. One day she would come back to this happy, glittering thing.

Very early, one morning in May, the sea was smooth and gold; the sky hazed; on the horizon a thin navy-blue line beyond which you could imagine Africa. Only the fisherman was there then, dawdling around his old caique anchored just off the shore, making a pretence of tending the thick, darkly-knotted nets that were draped over the deck and over the sides into the still water. He had been fishing that night, had sold half his poor catch to the taverna in the village and hoped to sell the rest to the housewives when the proper time for bargaining arrived. Now he was tired and there was little to do but idle in the boat near that one sandy promontory which, with its cluster of under-grown trees at the tip, marked the only break in the long shoreline and the only green in the brown-burnt landscape. Occasionally he whistled as he worked, totting up the night's catch into too small a sum in his head. In the still air with its promise of heat, his was the only movement, the only sound, for the sea was too smooth even to fret the grit at its edge. And the village behind the low dunes and the dusty vineyard, invisible from the shore, was silent except for the clapping of a cock's wing, silent in the early light of this day – any day.

The fisherman, having been up all night, stretched out on the deck, his brown young body in salt-white jeans, cradled his head on the smelly, damp nets, and slept.

It was after nine o'clock when he was awakened by a difference, but at first could not identify in what it lay. He raised his head with its rough sun-bleached hair. He was aware that his hair moved and his sweat was chill. A freshening breeze had sprung up. And now the thin dark line on the horizon was expanding slowly towards the land, though still at a great distance. The fisherman knew from his nineteen summers of observation that the gold sea in the foreground would eventually be obliterated by the deep blue of a surface ruffled by the late morning wind; that the sea would come alive and slap the shallow sands; that the trees would move. Already the breeze was shifting the sheen over the sky, which, at any moment, would blaze blue.

But there had been something else that had woken him – not the normality of the strengthening wind, but something unexpected. Now more clearly, being more awake and the sound nearer, the fisherman heard the shrill, high laughter and chatter of young girls, many young girls.

So he turned his eyes inland towards the village and saw, descending upon the beach from the path that led round the sand dunes and back inshore, the girls in their blue school overalls; and adults, teachers he supposed, among them. He watched as they struggled forward.

At the point where the hard, rough surface of the path ended in soft sand, some of the girls, shouting happily to each other, bent down to take off their sandals the better to walk – barefoot. But Anna stood still at the edge of the path as her friends pushed past her. She just had to stand and stare for a moment at the wonder of the wide water, see all the colours – glass green, song blue, secret purple – blending into the sky, falling into the sun.

'Come on, Anna,' called her friend, Maria, who was longing to get on, not to waste one vital second of this rare free day. 'What are you standing there for?'

But Anna did not hear her. She still stood and tried once more, urgently now as other girls were joggling and pushing round her, to take the whole of the sea into her eyes: the sea she had taken four years to find again.

'Anna, Anna!' This time she heard Maria, so bent down to take off her sandals, and splay-footed in the skittering sand ran shouting, 'Coming!' Hand in hand the two girls ran with all the other girls passing the slow teachers scrunching along in their authoritarian shoes.

The fisherman watched them as gradually, at different pace and speed, they all made towards the sea-line and the only shade. They congregated at a little distance from him under the trees on the promontory. He thought there must be about eighty girls. There were four adults – two men and two women. He supposed it must be a school excursion. He himself, unlike most of the other village children, had never been to school in the town and now there was hardly anyone left of his age in the village. They had all gone to find work in big places – the capital, the ports, even in foreign countries that were only names to him. So he regarded these unknown virginal girls with wariness; but he could not take his eyes off them.

The girls for their part, even Anna, had all noted

11

the young man by this time, had giggled more shrilly because he was there and because their lives were so tight with the old customs that any boy was a big adventure.

'You see him, you see him?' called Jane to Maria, and Maria to Anna. 'And the boat?' Some of the girls had already begun to speculate about the boy and the boat and the enormous possibilities of escape. And Anna laughed, 'Yes, I see it,' squinting into her friend's eyes and the sun, thinking that the boat could really and truly take her out far on to the free sea.

As they all, adults and children, circled and settled under the trees, the fisherman began to think of other things. He knew that the girls, being so young and of his own country, would not have the strange freedom of foreigners, but at least whoever came to the village would leave a few drachmas behind. Perhaps some small part of this would find its way into his pocket. It was time to go into the village and set about selling the rest of his fish. He stood up, tall, on the deck.

The teachers, seeing and hearing the excitement but not knowing the reason for it, thought it time to organise the day. They already felt slightly tired for they had been up since five. The three bus loads had left the central square of the inland town at six; for three hours they had bumped southwards over poor mountain roads until at last, swerving downwards in steep curves, they had seen the village which was their destination by the southern sea. For three hours they had jogged and sweated in clouds of dust while the girls sang and screamed at the top of their voices, celebrating in time-honoured fashion this one day away from the dingy schoolroom walls, the dull books that told them nothing. How glad the teachers had been to get out of the buses by the village church and walk down along the path, savouring the cool breeze and the warm smell of earth and growing things. It had been for them a tiny moment of release. But now they must organise. It would be a long day of responsibility.

Helen Mavrou, who taught Ancient Greek, said, 'These few trees will not give enough shade for all the children. And besides they will want water.'

The teacher of religion, Petrakis, said, 'We passed more trees on our way down from the village. The children could settle there. And there's bound to be a well or a tap in the village.'

The younger man said, 'One should be careful of well water. Typhus, you know.' He was Peter Vlassis, the one who taught maths.

'Then we shall want to eat,' added Helen Mavrou. 'The children have brought their own food.'

'The best thing then is to get the children to stay here while we go back to the village and explore the possibilities,' suggested Petrakis in his grating voice.

'But one of us had better stay with them.' The older woman was known as a worrier.

'I'll stay,' said the very young woman who had been silent until now. Margaret was new to the school. She taught French, a subject that had only recently been introduced, so that the other teachers regarded her as hardly one of them at all, almost a pupil herself. She had thus withdrawn into herself, giving the minimum, disappointed that she could not communicate her big ideas to her colleagues in the small town, hating its and their littleness, forgetful that deadness lay, at that time, over the whole country and that nowhere could a stranger have spoken.

Petrakis voiced the feeling of the other two when he said, 'No, no. I'll stay with the girls. You three go to the village.' And then to avoid any further discussion of the point, he raised his voice in a commanding shout. 'Girls! You will stay here all together with me.' The girls, in a reflex reaction to the harsh sound, fell silent, if reluctantly. 'Put your bags under the trees until we have found a suitable place for you to picnic. Do not wander away . . .'

'Sir! We're thirsty.'

'Sir! May we paddle?'

'Sir! There's a boat . . .

'Quiet. All of you, please. Very soon we shall find water for you to drink. You may take off your shoes and paddle.'

A few of the older girls sniggered at this: silly old fool for not realising that they were already barefoot.

'Nobody is to bathe of course. The sea is still very cold and besides most of you do not know how to swim. Is that understood? Nobody is to go near the boat . . .'

He glanced at the fisherman, as at an enemy.

14

'But, sir . . .'

His voice again cut through the clamour. Sullenly the girls turned their attention to the water. The teacher sat down self-righteously under a tree, pleased that his authority had, as always, quelled them.

Anna gazed out to sea as he spoke, not caring what he said. The darker water now cut the seascape into a geometrical half, the line dividing the distant broken surface from the nearer golden calm being hard and straight as a line drawn with a ruler. The line was much nearer. As if the horizon was coming to meet her.

Even the calm fore-sea was now moving slightly shushing against the shore. Sulkiness had left the girls, disappearing in squeals of delight as their bare winter toes were touched by the chill wetness and the hard wet grit. Only a few, more serious or more unloved, stood around stodgily still shod, or sat under a tree.

Cleo, lively and arrogant though only twelve and therefore 'little', left the excited group at the water's edge to shout to one of those solitary girls:

'Come on, Rena! It's not a bit cold. Why don't you come on?'

But Rena shook her head as if suspecting a trap. Cleo tossed her dark curls held in by the regulation school hair-band and rejoined the more adventurous ones, a vindictive expression on her face, which meant she was not going to talk to Rena again that day. So one of the two was lucky – through a chance remark so early in the morning.

Anna with Maria had wandered off from the main group of fourteen-year-olds who were now discussing the boat in earnest. They walked along the shore, their feet ankle-deep in the water. It was not that she was not interested in the boat. She was – vitally. But she simply knew that the teachers would eventually give way and the chatter bored her when all she wanted was the sea.

Meanwhile this group of older girls sent one of their number, Roubini, to persuade old Petrakis who was still sitting under the tree. They chose her perhaps subconsciously because she was a tall, well-developed girl – and pretty with her wide grey eyes. Roubini sat down next to the teacher, flaunting her femininity. 'You will let us go for a sail in the boat, won't you, sir?' she said softly, yet with a certain assured cheekiness, the degree of which she was able to control to a nicety.

'Certainly not,' replied Petrakis sourly, for he had really believed his authority, his little world of power with its precise place and function in the overall discipline, had been enough to suppress rebellion. He had even thought of relaxing. And besides he could not bear girls of that age. They were disordered and illogical. Well, so were all females, come to that. They did not fit into his neat world.

It was obvious that a 'Why not?' was on Roubini's lips, but she thought better of it, rose, flicked out her skirt as if brushing off sand or authority, and with a half-laugh, ran away.

'And don't go far,' shouted the man after her.

'No, sir,' she called back with perfect obedience in her voice, which irritated him extremely.

And so the girls wandered about the seashore in the strengthening sun, exploring for shells and pebbles, having as yet accomplished nothing more. One of them would lift her sun-hot face into the breeze and feel it cool. Some of them rolled up the sleeves of their blue overalls, while others reminded them that this was not allowed. Some of them even looked round for a means of escape from the promontory, but knew they could not get beyond the teacher sitting there on guard. Open revolt had never occurred to them. Anna and Maria walked as far along the shore as they dared, always conscious of that feeling behind them that they might at any moment be called back. And would have to obey. But Maria was getting a little bored because Anna did not seem, today, interested in any of the usual things they talked about.

'Let's go back and join the others – see what's happening,' said Maria.

'You go, if you like.'

Maria felt a little hurt. There was so much that her friend excluded her from. And Anna's parents were strange too: they didn't visit on name days when other people wore their best clothes, came and sat in the best room on the best chairs to eat cake . . . the father wrote – how strange! – and the mother often said things that shocked other mothers and fathers because they didn't know what she meant – but they seemed to understand about Anna and about being fourteen. Maria found she could talk to them. She liked that. And really she loved Anna and was rather proud . . .

Anna said, 'I'm sorry, Maria. All right, let's go back. Shall we dance – or what?'

Maria laughed. Anna bent and scooped up water in her hand pouring it over her bare arms. 'Look, Maria. Now it has no colour. It's just water.' She splashed Maria and they chased each other with the water, squealing and getting wet, but not caring.

They joined a group of girls who were standing as near as possible to the fisherman and his boat. They spoke in shrill excitement, not of the boy himself, but of the examinations soon to come and the distant carefree summer holidays, an unbelievable world of sun and long, hot boredom.

The fisherman still kept his distance, surveying them from the boat, waiting for whatever might present itself.

Meanwhile Peter Vlassis, Helen Mavrou and Margaret walked along the hot path away from the sea. Rounding the sandy rise, with its vineyards, they came to the olive-trees, a silver dusty shower of leaves above rough dark trunks splayed out to make three arms catching the spray of foliage and small green fruit, as yet unswollen. As they approached the village they passed the usual government slogans printed on the usual blue tin placards stuck on poles. They no longer bothered except for a passing quickening of older, buried feelings: Peter's careful indifference; Helen's doubts; Margaret's anger. Petrakis, when he passed the slogans which he and they would pass somewhere every day, felt satisfaction.

Then they caught sight of the village again: a few low white houses on either side of the path ending in and dominated, if such a word can be used for an almost equally low building, by the church. Just before entering the main part of the village, they discovered a fairly extensive olive grove, and by the side of the road a tap above a stone basin. On inspection, the tap proved to be working and when the water had been let to run a little it was passably cold. 'This will do,' said the 'French' girl – as most of the pupils called her. She was bored and hot. She had not wanted to come on the excursion but the head-master had ordered her to do so. Open revolt was for her, too, out of the question.

Helen Mavrou looked round carefully. 'Yes,' she pronounced in more measured tones. 'But some girls will be here and some will be by the sea. It is rather far. It will be a job looking after them all.'

Peter Vlassis said, 'Oh, I think we can manage. Besides there is no more suitable place. Now let's go and investigate the village for ourselves. Getting up so early, we shall soon be hungry.'

In the village street they found a small, dark taverna which fortunately had a vine-covered court-yard in front of it offering both shade and coolness. Peter said, 'Since we are here and the girls are in any

19

case being looked after, we might as well take the opportunity to rest and perhaps have a drink.'

But Helen was more bound in many ways. 'The girls are thirsty too. We ought not to delay.'

'By the time we've found out what's to be had here and ordered our lunch, we'll have had our drink and can be on our way refreshed.' He spoke blandly to ward off her and his own irritation, the two of them being at such odds in this and everything, but he really only provoked their separate uncertainties, and thus anger, further.

'No,' Helen said firmly to herself and him. 'I'll go back to the girls straight away and bring them to the olive-grove so that they can settle their things and have a drink of water. If you insist on staying here, then order lunch for the four of us.'

'All right,' he said. 'We'll stay and . . .' The rest of his words were lost to the woman who was immediately flustered by the impropriety – and on a school outing – of leaving the man and the girl alone together, while at the same time being drawn by duty back to the girls.

He repeated his question about the meal. She concentrated and said, 'Oh, fish, if they've got a fresh catch. Otherwise whatever they have. And a salad. Cheese perhaps – I expect it's made in the village. Don't be long. It's not fair to leave one person to do all the work.'

She bustled off, plump body in corsets and an overlong sleeved silk dress, feet hotly encased in stockings and shoes.

Peter, now sitting at the table in the courtyard with the girl, smiled at the thought of five minutes' respite in the day. He looked for the first time directly at Margaret who was wearing a shortish cotton dress, sleeveless, her long legs brown and bare. But she remembered the frustration of other conversations with him. He just did not understand whatever drove her to fury. And he was too shy to start again where they had last left off, not rightly knowing where that was, for indeed he did not know what drove her nor that his own blandness blocked her and him. He merely thought that she was too engrossed in her own opinions, which was a pity, because otherwise he might have . . . and she that teaching mathematics had not prepared him for the poetry and the power of life, which was a pity . . .

The fisherman had seen the three adults go and the rest of the party settle near or under the trees. As yet there was little indication of what they might do and he remembered that he had fish to sell. If he left it any longer without ice in the hold, the sharp-eyed housewives would not buy it. So he plunged down into the dark interior of the boat, arranged the fish on a large flat basket-tray and with this came up on deck again. Here he stood for a moment to survey as was his habit the sea over which the dark line was slowly advancing. And the girls. Then with a practised movement of his young body he slipped over the side and began to wade ashore. He did all this with careful grace though the thought was only a vagueness in his mind that perhaps one or two of the girls might be noticing him. In this, of course, he was wrong . . . . it was not that one girl was watching him: they all were, overtly or covertly, as they always watched, so bound by prohibitions, any young male. In those awakening years, to meet, marry and mate was inconceivable, a dream spiked round with 'don't's. The fisherman was as virginal as they.

Having gained the shore, the fisherman placed the tray on the ground, unrolled his jeans. He did not wear shoes. Then taking the tray again he balanced it expertly on his head and walking thus erect he gave the party a wide berth, as innocent of the girls' glances as they were of his. As he passed them at the nearest point he did not realise that he was the reason for the crescendo of their shrillness, nor did he know that with his passing they fell silent, listless, waiting.

Petrakis, still under the tree, felt that now he had the girls in hand. The enemy had gone. For one irritable moment he had thought that the young man was going to approach him, ostensibly to sell fish. When he saw that in fact he was going to take the village path, he heaved a sigh of relief and settled more comfortably under his tree. If it had not been that he was on duty – and besides the example he would be setting – he would have liked a cigarette. His wife often remarked that it was the only human thing about him, but even that one weakness was well-disciplined. Now he tried to distract himself from the desire and to make time pass by imagining the end of the day: himself at home with his wife and his baby son. He amused himself by recalling the antics of the infant and the numerous examples of his unprecedented intelligence – which just proved how wrong those people were who had warned him that an old man should not beget. Half dozing, he smiled. And even that small fact was noted by the girls, so that into the mind of one or two of them came the thought that old Petrakis would soon relent.

One small knot of fourteen-year-olds began to discuss what their strategy should be. For if one of the other teachers could be got on their side, could be persuaded to be the emissary, Petrakis might then himself be persuaded in the burning matter of the boat.

The boat had become for them a symbol of their battle against the adult world. Here was the sea so big and free before them and there was the boat that could take them on that sea. In the boat they could be at a distance from their teachers, or so they hoped. And the sea, unlike themselves, was boundless. With the old man sitting there so close it was not even worth turning on their transistors or record players to dance. Their dances he would most certainly not approve of.

'The "French" girl will support us. She wouldn't dare not.'

'Yes. But what's the use of her? She doesn't carry any weight. After all, Petrakis is the deputy head. Why should he listen to her?'

'Mm. Well, what about Vlassis then? He's young

enough to be on our side.'

'Him! He's stupid. He doesn't understand anything.'

'I say! Do you think the "French" girl is his girl-friend?'

Their laughter was breathless at the idea, and their eyes gleamed. For a while their heads were so full of possibilities that they all screamed together, one or another dropping out of the tight circle to double up with the fearful power of laughter.

Petrakis, hearing them, opened one angry eye, then seeing that they were merely indulging in some usual schoolgirl silliness, closed it again and went back to thoughts of his son, his heir who would carry on his name. He hoped that his wife would remember to give the child his vitamins at lunch time, a ritual which he normally supervised personally. But she would, he was sure. He had made a great point of it before going to bed last night. At least he had no problems of discipline in his own home. His wife always obeyed him, and so, he knew, would his son as he grew up.

Attracted by the laughter, other girls had joined the group and Roubini, the one who had tried to tempt the old man earlier, called the meeting to order. The others had always accepted that she was a leader.

'Our only hope,' she said in her clear high voice, 'is to enlist Mrs Mavrou. At least Petrakis will listen to her. She's very senior. And after all her husband is the headmaster, so he can't not listen to her.'

24

'Yes, but will she support us? She's always going on about duty and stuff like that.'

'I think she will. She's a worrier, but she falls over backwards to show us how much she understands us.' Vasiliki, a rival for leadership, made a comic grimace, her voice falsetto, as she said this. There was much giggling, for they knew it was the truth of caricature.

Roubini strove above the noise to maintain her position. 'I think she really likes us. And then there's her daughter.' The idea was sudden and triumphant.

'Oh, yes! The daughter. She's that little skinny thing over there. She's only in the first class, though. But we could easily bring pressure to bear, couldn't we?' Voula grinned wickedly. She knew all about pressure and in any case was determined to keep her position in the uneasy triumvirate of leaders, although she knew that Roubini and Vasiliki only tolerated her because she was a doctor's daughter and therefore usefully influential at times. Roubini, most of the time, could not bear her because of her veiled attitude to Vasiliki's poverty, the same attitude that Roubini's parents had when they constantly remarked: 'What do you want to have a friend like that for?' Which was why, though often in rivalry, Roubini loved Vasiliki.

Roubini, sensing the surfacing of undercurrents, magnanimously decided to make it democratic. As she put it to herself, for the word through misuse had gone out of use: 'It would be better for me if everybody decided, then they can't say it was only me.' So

25

she said, 'Which would be better? To go and ask Mrs Mavrou ourselves? Or to get the daughter to ask her?'

The girls were not used to having decision-making thrust upon them. Other people – adults – told them what to do. So there was much murmuring and fidgeting. But at last Vasiliki, anxious for her share in the day, dared: 'We'll get the girl to come with us. And we three,' she indicated herself, Roubini and Voula, 'we'll be the committee.' She was not quite sure where she had heard the word, but it sounded important.

'Perhaps she won't agree.'

'Who?'

'The little kid . . . what's her name?'

'Penelope. What a daft name!'

'She'll have to. We'll make her,' screamed Voula or Vasiliki or both.

The committee, now gloriously powerful, ordered a younger girl to go over and get Penelope, who promptly came, flattered by the attention of the older girls, but wondering and worrying like her mother. She appeared to be one of the neat orderly-looking girls who obviously obeyed to the letter all her father's – the headmaster's – moral instructions, imposed on him by himself and others, who themselves were imposed on by others right up the humourless hierarchy and right down to thin little Penelope herself: skirts below the knees, sleeves unrolled, hair either short with no side-curls or fringes or else long and plaited – in either case tamed and obedient under the regulation hair-band.

Normally Roubini and her friends would have withered the child with scorn, for they themselves were practised in walking the tight-rope between open disobedience and paying lip-service to the regime as represented in their lives by fathers and teachers. Their hair always escaped in some small way that could not be defined as outright rebellion, their sleeves were rolled up when unobserved, they tightened their belts around their child-waists so that their skirts were pulled shorter – but could cunningly appear long again merely by loosening their belts.

But now they were polite to Penelope – would you like us to call you Penny? – having something to gain thereby. Thus it was that a committee of four, including her own daughter, waited impatiently for the return of Helen Mavrou.

The fisherman was walking along the path between the vineyards. And the first person he met was the round, plump teacher bustling back to her thirsty charges. She looked hot and uncomfortable. The sun had by now thoroughly heated her tight clothes, whereas the upper body of the fisherman was covered merely by an open flapping shirt revealing his smooth tanned chest and stomach where the sweat was free to the air, cooling him. He almost felt sorry for this red-faced little woman with her grey hair scragged back in a bun. But from such he had learnt to expect suspicion, so he made his face and eyes blank as he passed her. To his surprise she gave him a pleasant 'Good morning'. She had been told that villagers expect to greet and be greeted even by strangers and that they would be offended if this were not observed. She would hate to hurt or offend anyone.

He was almost past her when he got over his surprise sufficiently to reply. His heavy rather sullen face lit with what she described to the others as a 'childlike smile' and he returned her greeting. But so sudden was the movement of his head that the tray of fish all but fell. It was only with a wild, swift circling movement of both hands upwards that he managed to save it from disaster.

'You nearly lost that lot,' said the woman kindly.

'Yes, madam.'

'Have you been fishing?'

'Yes.'

It was hard going but she persevered. 'Have you caught many?'

'No, not many.'

'What a pity.' She felt the inadequacy of this remark, recognising that she was ignorant of other people and their work, especially of village people, for how different the residents of even small towns thought themselves to be from . . . peasants. She tried to make amends.

'When did you catch them?'

'In the night. That's when the fish rise.'

'You were up all night?'

'Yes.'

'You poor boy! Well, I must hurry to my children. Goodbye.'

He too had exhausted his conversation for he was unused to speech and besides what topic was there in something natural, inevitable, like catching fish so that you and your family could live. He turned away with a mumble, embarrassed at his awkwardness.

He swung along gracefully, passed the slogan which he could not read, and soon came to the taverna where he had sold his first lot of fish much earlier that morning. The man and the girl had just finished their drink, but were still in conversation with the proprietor, a bony old man. He was known as Uncle Stathis in the village.

The fisherman heard the young man say, 'Well, that's settled then. Four plates of grilled mullet with oil and lemon. Salad. What have you at this season?'

'The lettuce is nearly over but it's not too bad. Then we have tomatoes but they're still a little unripe.'

Peter Vlassis turned in deference to the woman. 'Lettuce'll do,' she said indifferently. Vegetables came from shops and her theories did not reach down to the man digging and planting for a few coins.

Meanwhile the fisherman had gone on, his destination being the slightly richer houses near the church, where folk might not mind paying a reasonable price for his night's work. 'So Uncle Stathis has customers for the fish he bought from me,' he thought. 'I wonder how much he's going to charge them. I'll bet he makes a good profit.'

He turned round for a moment in speculation. The two teachers had risen and were standing in the pathway raising their hands in farewell. Faintly the fisherman heard the man's last words: 'All right then. Have all that ready for us at 12.30. We'll be along then.' He watched them go off down the path, and then turned towards his present business. He wanted to sell the fish quickly and then go back to the shore to see what was happening. The breeze stiffened against his body. The leaves of the olive-trees whispered together.

Helen Mavrou returned to the beach and immediately set about getting the girls organised. She told them to gather their belongings and follow her to the place near the village where there was shade and water. Some protested that it was too far from the sea, but she assured them that when they had established their base for picnicking and resting, they would be free to go back to the shore. 'As long as one of us is with you,' she said sternly. One or two of the bolder girls turned up their eyes and sighed, breathing 'Old fuss-pot!' She knew she was being annoying – in spite of her appearance she still quite vividly remembered herself as a young girl – but worry made her insist. 'There are so many dangers,' she said, not knowing herself whether she meant dangers from man or nature. She only knew she would be profoundly relieved to deliver them back to their homes in the evening. Ah! The evening: a gentle meal and chat with her husband, a comparing of their unaccustomedly separate days.

She informed Petrakis of the plans that had been made and he fell in with them, glad to have finished his guard duty. The two of them shepherded the girls away from the sea and along the path to the olive-groves. On the way, they met the other two teachers coming down, who, to avoid any criticism of their laziness, busied themselves with the children, helping them to get settled under the trees. One small girl had lost her packet of sandwiches and Margaret kindly offered to help her find it back on the beach, and elicited promises from some of the other girls that if it was not found they would share their food with her. The tears that had threatened vanished, and apart from a few squabbles about who should sit with whom and where, the party was soon ready and eager for the sea. It was still only ten o'clock in the morning.

On the way back, the committee of four found the opportunity to speak to Mrs Mavrou alone. They pushed her daughter forward.

'Mummy! They want to go on the boat.'

'Oh, dear! Do they? I really don't know if it's safe and besides Mr Petrakis has said no, hasn't he?'

'Please, Madam,' urged Roubini. 'People always go on a boat when they're on an excursion by the sea. And the water is so calm. We won't go far. You'll be able to see us all the time.'

The woman did not like being authoritarian, which in any case very rarely had the desired result. She believed in pointing out the pros and cons so that even children could make their own choices – in this she was very different from most of the other parents and teachers and, of course, from the rulers, but she had never, as Margaret had, thought of herself as in opposition, though sometimes, as now, every moment irked. She could think of no really logical reason why they should not go on the boat. She realised it was foolish to refuse from mere intuition – premonition almost – though this was strong and urgent within her. So reluctantly she agreed to speak to Petrakis on their behalf. 'But, mind you,' she added, 'no dancing or playing about in the boat. It's not safe.' Roubini said, 'Oh, no, Madam! We shouldn't dream of it.' Petrakis would have known at once how to evaluate this pious promise, but Helen believed what people said.

Behind the straggling group came the fisherman who had sold all but a few small fishes. Thank good-ness Nikos' wife had bought most of the best because she said that some foreigner was camping on their land and Nikos had promised to find fish. So he was fairly satisfied. He kept at a distance from the party in front, for some reason not wanting the adults to see yet that he had returned. When he finally rounded the last bend in the path, a new scene met his eyes. The girls were now spread out all over the sands, playing or clustered in groups. The older ones had removed themselves as far as possible from the teachers and had put a record player on a level stretch. One girl knelt in the sand by the instrument sorting out records while the others round her danced their own imagined versions of 'modern' dances – contorting their young bodies rhythmically into the provocative postures that Petrakis so loathed. He thanked God he had a son. On the other hand, Margaret and even Peter would quite like to have joined in, but were unsure of their position in this matter. Helen Mavrou noticed that her daughter, as usual, was not taking part in the dancing. She was quite thankful really. But thinking back, she realised she was being nagged by the unexpectedness of Penny's participation in the plea to be allowed to go on the boat, just as she had been so surprised that evening last week when Penny suddenly suggested that they should go to the sea. Perhaps, after all, it was a good sign, for she had often harboured the doubt that her daughter was too quiet, too obedient. 'But then she's still a little girl,' she thought. At that age in her class, some of the twelve-year-olds were already tall gawky women; others, like Penny, were still little match-stick girls who seemed only half their age.

The fisherman saw what was to be seen and then, as usual, swept the sea with his gaze. Three quarters of the sea was now dark blue. Only the strip near the shore was still unruffled, though now a swell, unbroken as yet, perceptibly and audibly moved the wet sand and the dead seaweed on the water line. By mid-day the whole sea would be choppy and the breeze would be really stiff and fresh. This was the normal development on most summer days. The fisherman merely noted the signs as a matter of course.

Thinking himself unnoticed in the background, he was in fact immediately observed by most of the girls and especially by the boat committee. They also watched the woman closely to see when she would approach the old man and put to him the question of the boat. The boatman had arrived. What else was she waiting for? Only Penny half hoped either that her mother would decide against bringing up the matter or that Petrakis would say no, because she was a little afraid of actually being on the sea, but naturally would not say so to her new important friends.

Cleo, the little girl with the dark curls, was a bright and plucky child, so though she was only in the first class and looked down upon, she knew what was in the air. She took it upon herself purposefully to play near the teachers, and the moment she caught the word 'boat' from the woman's lips, she was off in a skelter of flying limbs to report to the committee. At first she had to bawl the news through the racket from the record player. Vasiliki, who loved dancing when her life allowed and boasted of many imaginary boyfriends ('Really, dear! She's not at all a suitable friend for you!'), was in the middle of a particularly frantic wriggle when she understood that the news had arrived. She stopped dancing and shoved the disc-jockey hard. 'Turn that thing off!'

she yelled. The girl fell, spraying the instrument with sand.

'Oh! My record player! It'll be ruined with the sand!' cried Vana, who had been dancing.

'Never mind your silly record player. We've more important things to discuss,' snubbed Vasiliki. And such was her power and the power of the news that there was no back-answering. But very faintly her unkindness to Vana pricked her. She herself was so poor that to own a record player argued great wealth. She was not exactly jealous but made brusque by the hard struggle of work: not only school work but housework for a mother who had to take in sewing and stitch day and night just for enough to eat because her father was out of work. But she did not know that the record player was a hard-won toy, saved for by Vana's parents through a whole year because they saw how much their daughter loved and needed music. So Vasiliki did not know that she had provoked hate and that Vana would now avoid her. Vasiliki too would also avoid Vana through a guilt she did not want to be reminded of. One girl would be in one place and the other in another. They would not be together.

Cleo repeated the news and was the happy centre of attention. All eyes turned to the two teachers talking under the trees. The man could be seen gesticulating towards the boat as if he were demonstrating its unsuitability. The woman made smaller gestures which were difficult to interpret. Petrakis could never afterwards accurately recall what he had said and what she had said.

After a few minutes the man appeared to nod and shrug. Some of the watching girls in their excitement strained on tiptoe or grasped each other's arms. Petrakis then turned towards the sea as if he wished to hear no more. The woman left him and when the girls understood that she was approaching them, though slowly in the shifting sand, their joy bubbled and giggled out of them. The woman trudged on – she was overpoweringly hot by this time. Penny, in contrast to the prevailing mood, watched her mother sadly out of big eyes in a pale face. Other girls who had heard rumours of the negotiations joined the group. So quite a large crowd was present when Helen Mavrou finally reached them and said: 'Mr Petrakis has given his permission.'

Loud, long cheers greeted this announcement. Several girls bounced up and down; others clapped. A few looked doubtful. The older girls, who had tried to stay aloof from the general childishness, so far forgot their position as to look clearly pleased. They had won a victory. Anna nudged Maria and said: 'I told you so. I always knew we'd go out to sea.' Maria squeezed her friend's hand, slightly puzzled by a feeling that Anna was somehow giving a different emphasis.

Mrs Mavrou said, 'It now only remains to come to some agreement with the boatman. He will want money. There is the petrol he will use as well as his time and energy.'

This aspect of the affair had not occurred to the

girls. Some had money, some had not. Those without were soon assured that they would be lent money by the others. Nothing was to be allowed to stand in the way of this treat. The spurt of conversation about money died down as the woman approached the boy who had been loafing nearby.

Although he had sometimes taken people out in his boat, he had never dealt with such a large party. If he had a better boat . . .

But his father was too poor to afford one, so he had to make do. He was well aware of its age and condition, but it was stoutly built and he had never had any trouble with it beyond an occasional clogging of the engine. Besides he needed the money he would get from the girls. His father was too ill to work any more. All this now fell to him: fishing and tending the few olive trees and vines, selling eggs when the hens laid, making cheese and yoghourt from the milk of their half dozen goats. They scraped a living. There was his father who did little but sit on an old upright chair outside the front door looking into emptiness; his mother who helped when she could spare time from housework and spinning; his sister who helped in all the household trades – naturally, since she was a woman. His sister. She was older than he by two years and he must soon get her married. Of course she had to get married before he did – that is the way things had always been done in the village. But it was not that he himself was in any hurry – the idea of marriage just made him laugh. It was rather that a girl of twenty-one should not remain unmarried. There was nothing else a girl could do, otherwise she would become an old maid, laughed at and queer in the head. So any spare money he produced was put in the bank against her dowry and added to what his father had saved when he had been able to work. That was the awful burden of having a girl-child. Over the years the amount in the bank had grown, but it was still not sufficient. And then whom could she marry among the two hundred inhabitants of the village? The males now were mostly old men or very young boys. If she had had an education, if she had learnt 'letters', she might have got herself a job in the town. But would the father have let her go – alone? Would he himself want his sister to be 'free'?

These thoughts did not of course in their entirety pass through his mind at the moment of Mrs Mavrou's question, but they formed the vague, worried background to his nod of agreement.

Now the girls had a genuine supervised reason for open contact with the fisherman. They clustered round him. When? How many at a time? Where? How much money did he want? Five drachmas each, he said. That was an awful lot of money, wasn't it? He shrugged. He turned away as though indifferent. They, fearful of losing him, were ready to agree to anything and began searching their pockets, while others dashed to the olive grove where they had left their bags. Finally, every girl had five drachmas, her own or borrowed.

The woman had told him that there were eighty-five girls. He calculated, and realised that on half that amount of money his family could eat for nearly a month. They might even be able to afford meat on Sunday. The other half he would put in the bank for his sister – the next time he went to the town he would do that: when he had a good catch of fish to sell, or when the young beans were ready for market.

He would take them in four groups he decided, but his arithmetic was not very good and the silly crowd of girls was difficult to organise, even with the help of the teachers. Then he had forgotten to count the teachers themselves. But eventually he brought the boat round to the shore where they had all congregated again, then he helped aboard the first group – twenty-one girls and Mr Petrakis.

Petrakis told them to sit still and not to rock the boat. They could only obey. So they sat still and as they moved out, to the hot smelly puttering of the motor, the breeze caught their faces and penetrated to their bodies beneath the overalls, the sun shone in their eyes, and they began to sing the old sea-songs of their country:

A fishing boat set out with strong young men . . .

Petrakis summoned a fixed smile to show that he bore with it all, and thought alternately of lunch in the cool shade and of his son. The wind occasionally brought to his nostrils wafts of female sweat and he wrinkled his nose. The girls smelt the stale fish and salt of the fisherman's body. One girl whispered to another, 'Doesn't he ever take a bath?' And they sniggered together in a superior way, for they came

39

from a town of fifteen thousand people, where the houses had running water and some even had bathrooms.

By the shore you come, by the shore you go . . .

The fisherman, now that the engine was chugging along, stood by the rudder and steered. The dark blue line had reached just beyond the promontory and, having sailed beyond the trees, the boat crossed the line into rougher water. The little waves slapped at the sides and at the hanging nets. The girls who were sitting nearer to the edge of the deck, drew up their feet and squealed in fearful delight at every light shower of spray.

'I told you not to rock the boat,' Petrakis felt obliged to say.

The sea, the sea, my love . . .

In forty minutes they were back again. The next group was ready to go on board. This time there should also have been twenty-one girls, but friends were difficult to separate, or those who had been at odds with each other earlier manoeuvred not to be on the same boat. There was a lot of shifting about and at the last moment two more girls got off, deciding to go in the third or fourth boatload. So the fisherman started out on his second journey with nineteen girls and Helen Mavrou. She had tried to press her daughter to come with her, but Penny, enamoured of her success, an oasis in the lonely land of her childhood, wanted to stay with the committee of older girls. Helen would not force her opinion. They were slightly less squashed than the first group, were freer with the woman who joined in their songs and jokes, and on the whole enjoyed their forty minutes.

The third group of twenty-one girls with Peter Vlassis set off. By the time they were seen approaching the shore again, it was already late: well past noon. Everyone was hungry and the teachers at least were very tired. They were all over-hot from the sun. The last group was waiting impatiently. The leaders, Roubini and Vasiliki, were there, close friends always in spite of their rivalry and their difference in social class. Then there were most of the older girls: Anna, Maria, Voula, but not Vana who still nursed ill-feeling and had gone off in the third boat. There was, too, a smattering of younger girls: Cleo, the emissary, and Penny the go-between, both tolerated for services rendered.

The lateness of the hour held out hope that this group would be allowed to go alone without a teacher. Anna found that she too wanted this strongly. She felt there must be nothing alien when at last she met the sea. 'Please, please God, we don't want the adults,' she breathed to Maria with frightening intensity. Maria was almost shocked and looked doubtfully at her friend, but she only remarked that it was the 'French' girl's turn to go with them. 'Oh, she doesn't count!' said a girl who had overheard her. The 'French' girl could be dealt with. One of them had hidden a transistor under her overall.

Helen Mavrou really felt almost faint now and

longed for the shade of the taverna and the opportunity to sit down, to rest her swelling feet. Petrakis would, if pressed, take this last party of girls, but another forty minutes in the sun, another aeon of listening to raucous singing and silly female squeals, was almost more than he could bear. It was really Margaret's turn, but she was, she said, a very bad sailor and the sea was quite choppy now. Besides, she pointed out, there seemed to be quite a lot of girls in this group, so there really was not room for a teacher as well. When Petrakis saw that Helen was looking rather ill, he suggested that Margaret should take her at once to the taverna and wait there for the others. He and Vlassis, he assured Helen, would wait together on the shore until the last boat-load had returned safely. He did not think there was any need either for himself or Vlassis to take another turn in the boat, even if there had been room. Vlassis himself was indifferent and thought it did not matter either way. He merely wanted to get the whole thing over with, an attitude that was supported by the growing impatience of the girls already sitting in the boat and waiting for the outcome of the argument. Finally, the teachers all agreed that three times the safety of the trip had been demonstrated, the girls were behaving quite well, and the young fisherman seemed competent enough.

So Helen and Margaret and most of the girls who had already had their turn started off towards the village, to shade, water and food. Just before they turned inland by the vineyards, and when the boat had finally set off on the last journey, Margaret caught sight of a priest far on the other side of the promontory, on a path leading down to the sea from a low rise.

Although he was far away, she could recognise that he was a priest by the familiar black robe, billowing, and the tall chimney-pot hat. His robe seemed to be blowing out behind him. Either the wind had become stronger or he was walking in a great hurry. For a moment she thought she saw him gesticulate, but he was really too far away for her to be sure, and besides most of her attention was on helping Helen as quickly as possible to a resting place.

The fisherman, like the teachers, was tired now. He had not counted the exact number of girls for the last trip any more than the teachers had done. He certainly noticed, once aboard, that the girls appeared to be even more squashed up on the deck than the others had been. So much so that two or three girls had to stand upright holding the mast. On the part of the standing girls this was a manoeuvre more easily to dance to the music of the transistor even in that confined space, and even if they had to hold on to the mast while doing so. This music was their rebellion. Not for them the gentle songs of tradition that had been sung by the other girls on the other trips.

But as yet the girls were quiet and well behaved as they were still near the shore and in sight of the teachers. Petrakis himself had not counted the exact number of girls on this trip, for a fifth excursion was in any case out of the question. He supposed that bad organisation – not his – had led to this group being the largest. Vlassis, standing by Petrakis watching the boat go out, was glad the poor little kids were enjoying themselves. He often felt, in an abstract way, sorry for them in their grinding school routine. His greatest pleasure – professionally – was when he discovered the rare girl who really understood mathematics. But what was the point? Very few girls from the town ever went on to university; they stayed at home to exchange the routine of school for the dullness of marriage. Now Roubini was bright. He had hopes of her, but her parents would have none of it. What would a girl want with 'letters'? they said. Margaret, who was the only one who knew anything about it, had told him that one or two of the girls had talent in painting or writing. He knew she tried to encourage these little sparks that glowed here and there, but not with much success. The school syllabus left no time and the parents had no understanding. Except Anna's parents, he remembered. Margaret had told him the mother seemed quite pleased when she was told that Anna painted well. Anyway, it was all such a waste. Now if he had been sent to teach in a boys' school! So let them enjoy themselves when and while they could.

Twenty-four girls, unaccompanied, set out in the boat at mid-day. The whole surface of the sea was ruffled now and far out an occasional white-tipped wave could be seen breaking. But the fisherman who

44

had taken the old boat out in real storms was not worried. This was the usual noonday roughening caused by the cooling wind that always sprang up at this time of day. He might, he thought, even venture a joke or two since there was no teacher on board. In his innocence, he was entirely unprepared for the sly feminine teasing that started almost as soon as the boat had left the shore. And when they were out of ear-shot of the teachers, one of the girls turned on the transistor and the three or four of them standing round the mast began to dance, while the rest who had to sit, clapped rhythmically swaying together to the wild beat. The boy had to turn his eyes away and pretend to concentrate on steering. Once he did take courage to tell them to stop, that the sea was choppy and therefore they should stay still. But he was answered by such hoots of derision that, red-faced, he said no more. In his mind he decided to cut rather shorter this last trip, but again he reckoned without the girls who were fully determined to make theirs longer than the other trips.

Anna let the noise flow over her. It did not bother her. Nor did it bother her that Maria had chosen to sit over on the other side of the boat with more lively companions. Maria was always her friend, but Maria was free to choose – just as Anna was. So Anna sat dangling her feet in the water on the side of the boat away from the rough-knotted, humpy nets, themselves trailing along darkly, untended. She glanced round once at Maria over there expressing in her own way this big, strange thing called freedom. Anna's way was just to look and look out to the far horizon and then down into the clear green water beneath her feet. 'Green' was the word that came to her mind, but her eyes saw that it was really a rich fantasy of all the colours you could imagine shot through with wavering swords of sun penetrating to varied depths, here picking out a darting fish, there a round golden pebble furred with moss.

She remembered how the urge for the sea and its splendid breadth had first been born on that day when her mother had so impatiently tugged her away. Childhood, Anna thought, is a crystal ball circling round sometimes this way, sometimes that, its facets occasionally flashing with radiance; gleaming with grey lustre; or black. Childhood is not a straight line, so you cannot say: in this year I was a child and in that year I was not. To treat it, or indeed anything, as a series, is somehow to falsify. So she found it extraordinarily difficult to remember if that day with her mother by the sea was before or after that other day: an evening in spring it had been, when her parents told her that she must not go out into the street to play because there was a curfew. Now she knew, because they had told her, that it had been that day in April 1967 when the junta seized power. But then she had not even known the meaning of the word and had complied only when she saw the street so strangely empty of children – and her father so greyly sad. Since then she had become slowly more aware but did not really connect any of that with her present fierce joy at being at last in a boat on the sea. It was still her mother tugging her away that was most vivid in her mind.

'Why did you pull me away?'

'When, dear? I don't remember.'

'But you must. That's why I'm here now.'

'Perhaps you misunderstood. Children do.'

'Perhaps.'

'Mother, my friends never give me the right answers, either.'

'Perhaps you don't ask the right questions.'

'Perhaps.'

Her mother slowly faded from her mind, but in her mind she called after her: 'And that's why I'm sitting here and not joining in. I like them, I love Maria, but somehow . . . she's not enough . . . somehow I feel . . .'

From the deep green sea she lifted her face to the air, her whole body suddenly so vitally aware that she almost cried out in pain; she lifted her eyes to the burning whiteness of the sky and was for a moment blind.

On the shore the two men had been watching the boat until it was out of sight hidden by the trees on the promontory. They knew from the other three trips that the boat would not go far out to sea, but would cruise parallel to the shore and then return in perhaps half an hour. Petrakis looked at his watch.

'Half past twelve,' he said.

'Well,' said Vlassis, 'I think we've done our duty. They'll be back soon. I suggest we join the others at the taverna. We needn't delay our lunch any more.

47

In fact I told the owner of the taverna that we would be there at 12.30.'

Petrakis saw no reason to oppose this line of thought. The three parties had returned safely and so would the fourth.

'Besides,' he said, 'there are mainly the older girls on board.' Vlassis did not bother to point out how ignorant the old man was to imagine that age was a safeguard. Give him the little unformed, timid kids any day!

If the two men had waited a minute longer before turning away from the sea, they would have seen the boat appear again on the further side of the trees, but instead of continuing, as previously, close in to the coast, they would have seen it turn seawards. This under the scornful pressure from the leaders who instinctively caught at adventure and the breaking of bounds wherever possible; who ached for freedom. Helen Mavrou would have found it entirely natural since she prided herself on understanding the younger generation. Though she would have worried.

As indeed did some of the younger girls on the boat, who were rather scared of even the harmless waves that now slapped the sides of the boat and lifted the dangling nets. But neither they nor the fisherman dared voice disagreement. They were even more frightened of being teased and so were silent as the boat went out to sea.

As Petrakis and Vlassis turned inland, they too became aware of the priest. He was much nearer now. Vlassis thought he heard him shout. But the wind carried his voice back and away from them. He shrugged. If the priest wanted to say something he could come and find them in the village.

Within a few minutes, then, the four teachers were re-united, sitting comfortably and coolly under the vines outside the taverna. The table in front of them was still bare – after all there had been no need to hurry back – but sounds of preparation came from within the dark cavern of the shop. Margaret said, 'It's a good thing you told him 12.30. We may possibly eat at one.'

At that moment the owner, seeing that all his customers were assembled, emerged busily with a large sheet of white paper in his hand. This he placed over the wooden boards of the old table. But no sooner had he done so than the wind whipped it off again. After he had made several futile attempts to settle it, Vlassis got up and went to the side of the unmade road. He looked around and soon found four large stones. These he placed at the four corners of the table over the paper. The tablecloth thus ready, the owner disappeared again soon to return with a shallow basket in which were four hunks of dark bread. 'Baked by my wife,' he said proudly. 'Good! Village bread,' said Helen, now very much recovered. In the basket there were also four knives and forks.

'Oh, come! We shall soon be served,' said Petrakis, making an attempt at jolliness.

Helen, her feet no longer hurting, lifted her face

49

into the cool, steady wind. It had certainly become much stronger. Not only had it whipped the paper away so sharply, but now it was playing maliciously with the restless vines over their heads. It was blowing directly from the sea and since the olive grove was seaward of them, it carried the chatter and laughter of the girls who had started their picnic there.

'I'm so glad the children are enjoying themselves,' remarked Peter Vlassis, to show interest.

'Hm,' grunted Petrakis.

'I only hope they don't get too sunburnt,' said Helen, aware of the irritating inevitability of her remarks. 'My daughter was already complaining of a headache. I should have brought a hat for her. I didn't really want her to go in the boat at all. Such a long time in the sun and no shade on the deck. But you can't persuade children.'

'Hm,' said Petrakis.

Margaret said, 'Oh, I shouldn't worry.'

The smell of grilling fish was now very definitely coming from the open door of the taverna. The owner brought out the cheese and salad. They started to eat.

Munching, and therefore comforted, their attention was momentarily diverted by a figure striding down the road from the higher end of the village towards the sea. The figure was tall and brown and lean. It was clad in faded blue jeans over which a yellow shirt flapped loosely. This appeared to be the uniform of the foreign young – and regrettably some of their own young too, despite government decrees against girls in trousers and boys with long hair. Yet the age of this person was difficult to guess. The hair was long and fair, untidy towards the shoulders and blown back by the wind. If nothing else, the very pale blue eyes and the fair tan would have suggested a foreigner. The bare feet were covered by leather-thonged sandals. 'Like Christ,' murmured Margaret, but Petrakis did not think this an apt remark. He thought it was in poor taste and he did not like to be reminded that the idle, drug-addicted young – as he thought of them – so often did look like Christ. It offended his logicality, for Christ was nothing if not remote, cruel, Byzantine.

Helen said, 'But is it a man?' She flustered on, 'I mean he could be a woman . . .'

They argued mildly about the sex of the figure who had now passed them with long, loose strides.

The fish arrived and was golden-brown, full and succulent.

Before starting on it, Helen again lifted her flushed face into the wind. And borne faintly on that wind she heard the cries of young female voices. She stopped and listened, as did the others seeing her arrested movement.

Peter Vlassis bent towards his fish, fork in hand.

'They are only playing,' he said.

2   The Nets

Strange, here I see the light of the sun; the
*   golden net*
where things quiver like fish
that a huge angel draws in
along with the nets of the fisherman.
                    George Seferis: 'Agianapa I'.

The old priest, despite his age, still
served four villages, two on the coast and two further
inland on the lower slopes of the mountain. On
Sundays and holy days he would always try to get to
two at least of the villages in his care, so that none
would be too long unshepherded. He would say
mass very early at one of the coastal villages and then
walk – as he was walking now – five miles along the
shore, in storm or sun, to the other. Or he would get
a donkey to take him up to one of the mountain
villages on a Saturday evening, spend the night with a
friend, say mass early there and then continue on
foot to the next one, higher, more barren yet.
Strangers would wonder to see the old man with his

long white beard walking such a distance, but to the villagers there was nothing strange. He was a good old man and even the half-doubters would take pride in him, offering the strangers such information as: 'He's a saint. He lives on bread and onions.'

He had led a happy life, baptising, marrying, burying. He gave comfort to the mourners over the traditional brandy and coffee. He was not adept at words concerning Paradise, but tried at least to lessen the grief of one whose husband, wife or child had been taken to the Underworld. Myths were muddled in his mind, and in the minds of his people. There was an old damp-stained fresco of St Michael in one of his churches. He was not at all sure the villagers were right in calling him Charon, but they believed that the saint's job was to take the souls of unbaptised babies to the Underworld. And then again he could never quite understand why the bishop insisted on calling another church 'Holy Apostles'. Everyone knew it was 'St Peter's'. It was all something to do with something called the Schism. But did it really matter?

It was the natural course of life in his villages that mattered. On the whole, in the priest's life and in that of the villagers, there had been neither great joy nor great sorrow. Once a young shepherd boy had fallen from a rock; once a woman had died in child-birth. The doctor, like the priest, served several villages which he visited on horseback. But some-times he could not be called in time. Once a young man had committed suicide, but these were rare events in the fifty years of his priesthood and he had never had any reason to complain to God. True, his own wife had died in middle-age and they had had no children, but, he would shrug, all that was natural enough.

He had been a simple boy, not over bright at school. His parents had been very religious so from an early age the boy sang in the church choir and later was a censer-bearer. The church and its safe, orderly calendar was part of his home life. His mother had supervised the fasting – no meat, fish, poultry, eggs, butter or olive oil during Advent and Lent; and the huge feasts that followed: the turkey at Christmas and the spitted lamb and red-dyed eggs at Easter. This was all done unquestioningly and presented no hardship: in his simple faith Easter was the inevitable consequence of Good Friday. Yes, he had been on the whole happy and even his mother's death had been at least accepted – the doctor had told her to have no more children, but the priests had said that this was a sin. He had not doubted that. All the people of his village had been like that seventy years ago. It was something that bound them together when no foreigner had ever penetrated their poor, bare land. But today, the old priest often sighed, things were changing. In Lent even the women – usually so much more observant of religion than the men – would come to him in confession and say, 'Father, the doctor told me that I shouldn't fast all the fifty days. It's my anaemia you see. He says I must eat meat. Is it a sin?' And the priest was obliged to say that the church gave dispensation in the case of illness. It often seemed to him that illness was on the increase and he wondered whether it was not that faith was becoming fainter, just at a time, too, when a strong faith was more necessary than ever with all the terrible things you read about in the newspapers: wars and violence and people going to the moon, masons and protestants and tourists. Some of the tourists he had seen were boys and girls with no wedding ring between the lot of them. But did it matter, he often thought again, as he walked in the early light of Sunday morning. He knew God was there. He was a little vague about details, but he knew. Of that he was sure.

It had been natural for him when he had just scraped through school to go on to the seminary in the town, where he learned to read the Byzantine liturgies, to intone, to give the stock answers to stock questions. While in the seminary, he had married as the law of the church ordained, for you could not be a priest without a wife. On the other hand, you could not rise in the church unless you were a monk and celibate. He had thought about that, but he knew that he was too simple ever to become a bishop and somehow he could not leave the village with all the familiar neighbours, the laughter and the noise of life. But he had been attracted to the monastery, high and lonely on the mountain top. He had thought at one time that it must be wonderful to worship God in all that silence and through the monastic hours – from three o'clock in the morning until late at night.

Once a monk had said to him, and this had impressed him greatly, 'Only we are awake and praying for the world when it is asleep. If we did not pray in those dark hours when Satan comes, what would happen to the world?' But regretfully he had decided that this was not for him, so unlettered in theology and so loving his small world. Yet, although he had never been able to rise beyond his poor villages, his parish, which hardly gave him enough to eat, he had been happy all his life. Only when some would-be clever man in the village questioned his belief in God, would he shake his head in puzzlement, strive for an answer that he could not express, and say his prayers lest the other man's devil enter his own head. At such times he was hurt and bewildered, but it never lasted long.

The churches that he had not been able to visit on a Sunday, he would try to visit during the week. Of course it was not the same: few people had time on a weekday – the men in their fields, the women fetching water, washing clothes at the stream, and, well, you couldn't persuade the children on a weekday, not even in the holidays. In his youth, things had been different. But he continued to visit the villages though it tired him a lot more now than it used to, but perhaps he gave joy to a few old women, and to God. At the same time he could always drop in on an afflicted house. Last week he had been asked to say the prayers for casting out the evil eye. A woman had terrible pains in her chest and believed that it was a neighbour's doing. She had already gone to an old witch to get a magic charm, but the pains had persisted. In despair she had thought of calling the priest though she was more frightened of the old magic than believing in the new. She was a 'good' woman and always went to church and fasted. She saw no contradiction in this. But the doctor had told the priest that she in fact had cancer, so the priest knew that his magic would not work either. He could not tell her this and besides the word 'cancer' must never be said. It was always 'that illness', in case the word itself had evil powers. The same monk had said to the priest in his youth, 'If you believe in God you must believe in the Devil.' He had never forgotten this either.

Today he had been to the other coastal village and was now walking along the shore path between the two. He had visited an old woman who was mourning her husband. He had buried him ten days ago. Just to have a visitor, just to talk, gave the poor old creature comfort. The conversation had taken the usual way on such occasions:

'Life to you.'

'Life to you.'

'May I come in?'

'Sit down, father. I will get you brandy. Or would you prefer a little coffee?' The old woman had spoken from beneath the heavy black veil that covered her face, and she made as yet no move, sitting blackly in the corner of the one big downstairs room on a hard chair. The room was overfull and heavy with pictures: many icons, huge old photographs of whiskered men and high-laced women, and gaudy paintings of romantic lovers standing in bright green forests or by blue seas in orange sunshine. When the priest had settled himself on another such chair and had folded his arms within his wide sleeves as was his manner in repose, the old woman again showed signs of life.

'Ah! He was a good man. A warrior when young. Now he has gone to the Underworld.' As she spoke, she began to rock back and forth, wailing, as was expected of her. When the woman had wailed enough she would stop. Thus was sorrow measured. At a funeral, people would watch the widow and comment to each other: 'See how she cries. She must have loved him.' Or if the widow was cold and frozen in her private grief, the tongues would say, 'Not one tear did she shed. She can't have loved him.' Privacy and the individual act were unknown to these people, so bound, lest perhaps they fall.

The priest now thought it proper to interrupt: 'Charon has taken him. He was a strong man. I remember him as a boy . . .' In fact the dead man had been older than the priest, but he thought he remembered him as a boy. It is not necessary to be exact.

'A little coffee?'

'Thank you.'

'You have a long walk.' The woman at last detached herself from the chair and shuffled over to the other side of the room where an old plywood cupboard housed her best coffee-service.

When he left, the priest thought that he had probably given her a little comfort, though he was ignorant of the words to use. And as he walked along the shore between the two villages, on a path higher but parallel to the sea, he was happy, for all this was in the nature of life.

The sun was bright and hot on his face, dazzling his old eyes, so that at first the shore and the distant promontory were hidden in a golden mist. But as he very slowly drew nearer, he saw that strangely the beach was covered with blue figures, some running, some still. But they were a blur to him. A boat – it must be the old fisherman's he thought, there was no other in the village apart from that of the old pagan – was close inshore. More blue figures were getting out of it. And as he came still nearer, though still far, he could distinguish more, many more, getting in. They completely covered the deck, while some seemed to be standing near the mast. Too many, surely? He tried to quicken his pace, but he could not at his age. Who would be in charge of the boat? The old fisherman was now incapable because of his arthritis. Oh, the cursing of God that the priest had pretended not to hear.

'How I suffer,' he had roared the last time the priest had seen him. 'May the devil take it, how do you explain my misfortunes, old man? An idle son, a daughter with no dowry, a complaining wife, never enough money. Last year all my vegetables got blight and I had to throw the lot away. And now this pain. And you sit there and talk to me about God . . .'

The priest cut him short before he could blaspheme, and in fact was wrongly accused because he never talked about God. He didn't know how to. He said mildly, 'Our sins . . .'

'Ha!' responded the old man fiercely. 'God looks after those who really sin. It's the poor innocents like me who suffer. I did my duty – married, had six children and buried four. I've worked hard all my life, minded my own business, never had another woman, and look at me! No, old man, it's the real sinners that are the lucky ones.'

The priest had hurried away as soon as he could, the fisherman's bitter cackle following him, because he really did not know how to answer these terrible words. Since then, he had avoided him and did not like to protest that his son never came to church.

So it must be the boy who was taking the boat out. A stupid boy and an old leaky tub, an overcrowded tub. These thoughts joined together in the priest's mind as his old bones tried to hurry on and they added up to one word: 'Danger'.

The boat was now pushing out from shore. Many of the other blue figures – he now began to realise that they must be schoolgirls – were leaving the beach by the path leading to the village. He discerned two figures that were not blue. They must be the adults in charge. As they also began to turn inland, he waved frantically. He thought that one of the figures had seen him, for he saw the whiteness of a face momentarily turned towards him. But they both hurried on and disappeared from sight.

The sea was choppy and a fresh wind had sprung up. The rim of the priest's chimney-pot hat cut into his forehead. He was still far away. A young man might have covered the distance to the beach in five minutes, but it would take him twice the time. When the boat was well out to sea and the shore empty of all the other girls, he noticed two men standing by the water looking out to sea. He shouted but they did not hear him because the wind was blowing from them to him and blew his words away. He hurried on, tired now, his heart thudding painfully beneath his black robe. The two men now left the shore and turned inland. He shouted again. One of the men turned his face towards him. Surely he must have heard the word 'boat' which he bellowed out with all the force of his age-deepened voice. But once again he was ignored. It was vitally important to catch their attention. But he slowed for a moment. His body could not keep up the pace. And, after all, what could he do? The boat was now far out – that fool of a boy! Perhaps, though, it would be all right. The boat was turning at last. It was approaching the promontory. The priest was nearly there now. He was the only one on that wide brown shore. He reached the landward side of the headland and stopped, pulses racing, body bathed in cold sweat, striving for breath. He blinked his eyes free of rheum and sun-dazzle. The boat came into focus. He could see it well now. And the girls on the deck. It was full of young girls, a mass of blue, and faces, many faces topped with hair fair or dark. He could not distinguish individuals, only the mass. But he recognised the fisherman's son standing tall among them at the helm. The priest was calmer now that he had arrived and could be motionless, now that the boat was fast approaching the land. Perhaps he had just been a foolish old man, who had dreamt up fear from nothing.

Penny's head ached. The sun was burning on her forehead and into her eyes. Even if she screwed them up she could still see a horrible red light. And there was no way of changing her position, squashed up as she was among legs and arms and bodies. She wished now she had not come to this hot, boring place. But in a way it had been worth it because the girls, especially the older ones, had at last taken notice of her. One day she would really do something stupendous so that everyone would admire and envy her. As soon as she got the opportunity in any case she planned to tell them that it was she who had suggested the sea to her father, the headmaster. Then they'd really have to take account of her, wouldn't they?

It had been one day last week when she had been having supper with her parents:

'Eat up, dear. You really must try to eat a bit more.'

'I've had enough, mother.'

'But . . . how will you ever grow big?'

'Leave the child alone, Helen. She says she's had enough. Now, Penelope, what about your homework?'

'I've done it.'

'There's a good girl. I wish the other girls were as attentive as you are. Could you manage your algebra all right?'

'Yes, Daddy . . . Daddy? Have you decided where the school is going for the excursion next week?'

'Not yet. I thought you might go to that new archaeological site they've discovered. It should be most interesting. Your mother could give the girls a talk about it – explain it to them. I can't come, unfortunately, with all these examinations to prepare.'

'But Daddy the girls don't want to have to look at things. I mean, if we've got to go on an excursion because – like you said – the government has ordered every school to go on one – well, at least let's . . . I want to . . . do what I like. I'm tired of listening to people telling me things. I have to put up with it every day at school. I hate school.'

Their first reaction was one of shock, as though she had destroyed their very reason for existence. The child had never spoken like that before, had never really expressed any personal feeling about anything. The father then realised that perhaps this was the moment he had been waiting for – the moment of communication with this solemn, dull little girl who was his daughter. Sometimes he felt it was his fault.

The mother more instinctively got up to encircle the child with her loving arms. But Penny flinched away from her and the father gave Helen a look to show her that he would deal with it.

'Tell me about it, Penelope.'

Penny jumped up and rushed out of the room. She got ready for bed, in her usual self-contained way, dreading the ritual goodnights. Tonight she was sure they would come into her room for an understanding talk, try to draw her out. She longed, as she did every night, for the moment when she would at last be alone, the light out, the door closed, alone with herself and her thoughts, her dreams in which she was a person of consequence, able to leave home at any moment she chose, free to roam the whole wide world. Answerable to none. Acclaimed by all. Perhaps sometimes she would visit her parents in her big, shining car. In her dream she was always tall and very beautiful with round breasts.

The father, wanting only to please her, decided that the school would go to the sea.

Oh, how my head aches! The sun, the glare, the girls . . . I wish . . . I wish . . .

The blue mass moved and heaved and in a second it happened. The boat keeled over, sliding its load, a tangle of shrieking children, from its now vertical deck. With them, a darkness too might have been seen to fall, with them and among them. The water was frantic foam. Then gracefully the deck fell further over the place where the water moved, and now there was only the upended hull, black and big.

The old priest ran forward a few steps – really ran – but as his mind caught up with his feet, he realised that he could do nothing himself. As an urchin, he had played with the other boys in the water but he had never learnt to swim. In any case he was old and weak. He therefore turned and ran back a few steps. Again he stopped, magnetised by the cries that were now, after the first immense scream and the following silence, louder, clearer, more vitally needing. Surely he should not turn his back. So for a second or two he thus dodged backwards and forwards like an idiotic hen.

Finally he teetered more definitely towards the village, at last knowing clearly that his only hope, their only hope, was to fetch strong young help as soon as possible. At the entrance to the path, he tangled into a group of girls descending on the shore from their picnic among the olive groves. They were ready to greet him politely, some to kiss his hand, while he was trying to summon the words from his labouring lungs to tell them of the boat, to tell them to run run run because their young legs were swift. But at that moment of meeting, they caught sight of the overturned boat just beyond the trees and stood rooted with mouths open. Then before he could get out any word at all, they turned, as one, and fled back up the path to the village, buffeting him aside.

He was still plodding wearily up the sun-struck path, when he was met and overwhelmed by the human tide flowing at all speeds in all manners down to the beach. So he turned with them and was soon left behind save by a few of the very slow and the very old. And as he moved, he muttered, 'I told them so. I told them that the boat was dangerous. But nobody listened to me.'

Some of the girls picnicking under the olive-trees had already finished and, not wishing to obey instructions to rest, had started to go back to the beach to greet their friends who had elected or been elected to make up the fourth party in the boat, now judged to be due back. A few minutes later these girls were seen to be racing back along the path towards the village and their teachers.

Having all but trampled the old priest, not stopping to understand his confused cries, they raced headlong, legs gawky or plump flying and flailing, though to them their progress seemed overslow, sticky as in a nightmare. They passed without noticing a tall fair figure, who had to side-step sharply in order to avoid them.

This person stood on the grassy verge looking in the direction of their flight, but realising that there must be some urgent reason for their panic, their gaping mouths, their eyes staring in faces white beneath the flush of heat, decided that it would be better, would waste less time, if she continued towards the sea and the source of their fear. She broke into a long-paced run.

The teachers in the taverna, now almost at the end of their meal, became aware that the brown path and the shimmer of air above it was no longer empty. Blue figures were filling the space, at first two or three, then more and more crowding in a thick mass. The original group had been swelled by the rest of the picnickers as they passed the olive grove. The terror of their flight had drawn the others after them uncomprehending. Now they all ran towards the teachers, silently.

As they approached, the four adults stared blankly because their minds could not at that moment and for many moments, contain any more ghastly thought than that it was all some childish matter to be smoothed over. Only Helen Mavrou made a vague connection in her mind between the running girls and the cries they had previously heard.

The first, the swiftest girls, arrived at the taverna. They gasped and spluttered, spoke all together or not at all with wild gestures in the direction of the sea. One child, hardly more than an infant so tiny was she, irritated beyond endurance by the impassivity of the adults and her own inability to communicate, grabbed the hand of Petrakis and pulled and pulled. But he resisted because he and none of them yet understood. At last the words 'boat' 'girls' 'sea' emerged from the babble and broke into their minds. Somehow the adults pieced together some tentative connection and, their minds white with a nameless horror, they began to run down the long path accompanied by all the girls. The older woman jogged and spurred herself on painful feet with her daughter's face, thin and overwise, before her eyes; the older man made a violent spurt despite his age; the two younger teachers outstripped all except a few girls whose reaction was to reach the sea as soon as possible. Other girls did not even try to compete. Either their legs were already too weak to carry them, or else they did not dare to see whatever was to be seen and so moved draggingly, weeping or with hand to mouth to stay the fear.

As they all ran or lingered, they were joined by the villagers, as ignorant as they of the true events: old women in black crossing themselves; men of all ages strong enough to run – these were the most purposeful and reached the shore a very few minutes after the stranger; the priest, who was the only one who knew but was utterly unable to speak even if anyone had stopped to listen; the owner of the taverna still wearing his apron; Nikos and his wife on whose land the 'foreign' woman had camped; the little village children crying like birds in a storm and getting in everyone's way. They all knew something, the dread words having fled from mouth to mouth, and yet knew nothing. They all streamed down the path towards the sea.

The strange woman was in any case the very first to arrive. And this was fortunate because she was, of all, the most cold and capable. She was not a foreigner as most had thought, but from a northern city of this country where she was a doctor, director of a large hospital. And being a woman in this man's land had had to fight with the weapons of coldness, calculation and efficiency. She had fled to this tiny village on this remote shore for a holiday from overwork and from people. She had wanted, for a few days, to be quite alone.

When the doctor rounded the last bend she saw at once the completely empty beach and the overturned boat. She was for a moment reassured by the fact that it seemed so close inshore. It lay just beyond the promontory. The water round its dark hulk was being churned and thrashed by many arms. Cries for help rose shrill on the air. The doctor reckoned that if she ran to the tip of the headland by the clump of trees she would be very near and could help the people get ashore. Not having been on the beach in the morning, she did not know who or how many had been on the boat. As she ran, she pulled off her shirt and began to unbutton her trousers – fortunately she was wearing her swimming suit underneath, for it had been her intention to swim when she had set out from her tent on Nikos' land higher up beyond the village. She was very nearly there now and she kicked off her sandals as she ran. The thought flicked across her mind that the cries were very youthful.

She arrived at the trees a full two minutes before the able-bodied – the men of the village and the two younger teachers – could possibly arrive.

Poised, at the water's edge, she first briefly took stock of the situation. Her instinct, from rigid training and self-discipline, was not to plunge in heroically and regardlessly, but to decide first on the best and most logical way to help. The upturned boat towered over the thrashing water perhaps fifty yards away. It seemed to her, in the few seconds it had taken her to run the length of the beach, that the noise and movement in the water had become less. Now she had expected to see people swimming towards the shore – a very short distance – but instead she was appalled to see seemingly lifeless bodies just below the surface, the waves washing over the faces and into open mouths. Those that could be seen above the surface or clinging to the steep slippery sides of the hull, all wore blue. With a shock she realised that they must be schoolgirls. Only one figure was different: a male lay athwart the hulk high above the water.

A split second was necessary for her eye to report to her mind. She plunged into the sea at the moment that the conclusion hit her: 'My God! They can't swim!'

She had driven down from the northern city during the last week in April, through lashing rain, to head south into the sun. She hoped the hospital would be able to solve its various problems, but she determinedly put all thoughts of it and of work out of her mind. She even tried not to think about those other men and women who came so secretly at night, depending on her for the co-ordination of their plans. She must rest just for these few days. The next day she had taken the ferry from the fuss and fumes of Piraeus to a southern port. At last the sun shone. She did not stay in the port but immediately took the road south over wild mountains where eagles circled the stone-walled sheep pens. The road ran down to a small town in a valley. It was mid-morning when she passed through the central square. She would have liked to stop for a drink, but knew her 'otherness' of clothes and manner, the very fact that she was a woman alone, would have drawn the comments of the inhabitants however 'advanced' they thought themselves to be from their experience of foreign tourists. So on she went and passed a school outside which girls in blue overalls were walking, reading, talking, eating. It must be their break. The blue and white flag of Greece fluttered on a pole in the centre of the dusty, enclosed school courtyard.

She went on and on away from the town, seeking the unpeopled places that existed in her mind. She passed an old man on a donkey, a little girl tending sheep with a big rolled umbrella crooked over her arm. Was she still expecting rain? An old woman plodded along the barren road with a huge bundle of brush-wood on her back, so bent that one wondered if she could ever have walked upright. A young woman with a high coiffure teetered along the road on broken high heels. Where was she coming from? Where was she going – all dressed up? The doctor felt herself to be the foreigner they thought she was in this, her own land, for the villages were indeed foreign to the towns and they to them in ignorance of the life that gave them food.

The doctor in the safe enclosure of her car felt free to wonder at humanity. And at last with the sun well beyond its zenith and dying towards the west, she came to a village by the sea. Here the road ended. She could go no further.

Once she was in the village, the sea could no longer be seen. She knew only that it was there, having observed the lay-out of the land from the thyme-covered slopes of the mountain before the road plunged down. The green of the strongly scented bushes had been dusty and almost the only green at all in that tawny landscape. The orange sun had cut a path of fire through the copper water.

On the flat coastal plain she came first to a few white houses tucked into groves of orange and olive. She knocked on the door of one of these houses. The woman who answered the door was large and white, her uncorseted body flowing to the utmost limits of a red floral robe. Several young children, dressed in a clutter of garments, clung to her skirts. Mother and children at first just stared at the strange woman who stood in their doorway. The doctor asked if she could camp in the orange grove behind the house. The woman seemed flustered as though the doctor had spoken in a foreign tongue. But then she nodded and calmly disappeared with her children. Soon she was replaced by a handsome red-faced man. He must be her husband – his features had been copied five times in the faces of his children – though he looked younger, and whereas his wife was soft and fluid, he was hard and chiselled.

'Que voulez-vous?' he said.

The doctor was amazed, but then with a rare smile she said, 'I too am Greek. May I camp on your land?'

The man laughed loudly. His wife and children came round him at the sound and they too laughed when the mistake was explained to them. The woman, wiping her eyes at last, said, 'We took you for a foreigner. You're so different, not like a . . . like our women.'

She asked the man, Nikos, how much money he wanted to let her camp there and use the water from the well. 'Nothing,' he said. She protested. 'Nothing,' he said again firmly. So she prepared to settle down in the orange grove. She put up the tent in a spot where she reckoned the noonday sun would not beat too fiercely on it. She arranged her stove, her utensils, her bed. While she was thus engaged, the woman came out of the house to stare at her from a short distance. The children still kept close to her but seemed a little bolder now. One of them darted away from his mother towards the doctor. The mother ran forward to pluck him back, so gaining ground nearer to the strange woman to whom she gave a small smile that could have meant anything or nothing. Her eyes were black with curiosity.

The doctor loathed being watched, had not imagined, as she escaped from her usual life, this peculiar form of invasion into her privacy. She felt like a theatre and thought in a flash of humility that she must indeed be a theatre to these people who had no entertainment except human drama. They had never known the cinema; television had not yet penetrated their mountain barriers. So it was not unnatural that apart from the woman of the house a crowd of neighbours and their children had gathered too in the roadway to watch.

She carried on with her preparations feeling acutely embarrassed. At last she decided to risk some show of spirit. She straightened up from her tasks with a gesture which clearly said that she was finished, and which she hoped would be interpreted as meaning that the show was over and the audience should disperse. The woman, instead of taking the hint – to her it was inconceivable that you should not want people around you – came even nearer. The others outside shifted and whispered together.

Now the woman was standing right beside her and could not be ignored. Besides, the husband had refused money and placed her under obligation. The woman smiled up into the doctor's eyes. She seemed not yet convinced that they spoke the same language and indeed the doctor at least had found it hard to understand the heavy dialect of Nikos and his wife. She showed her wedding ring and then pointed to the doctor's own ringless finger. She deeply resented the direct question between strangers. She reddened, unwilling to answer simply because, in any case, the answer was not simple. The woman now seized her hand and made a gesture of enquiry. The doctor felt her spirit squirm at the intimacy of the hand but could no longer with any politeness evade. 'No, I am not married,' she said shortly.

The woman smiled sympathetically and patted her arm. Again the doctor squirmed. She felt, with her face so red and the audience to make matters worse, like a naughty schoolgirl found out in some ridiculous misdemeanour. She felt in fact that she had failed them by not being married. She was lacking in their eyes and for an instant in her own. She resolutely refused to offer the information that she was a doctor. Either they would find it too incredible to be believed, or the village women would at once come crowding with their children to wait upon her white magic.

As a means of escape from the situation which she would later describe as a 'culture clash', for the old ways of the country had long been overlaid in the cities by an industrial veneer, she said that she was tired and dived into her tent. After half an hour of this stuffiness she thought it safe to emerge, and indeed Nikos' wife had gone indoors and there were fewer people about. She took a camp stool and sat outside the tent with a book in her hand which she could pretend to be reading if further attentions threatened. She did not realise how bizarre a sight was a woman reading a book.

The crowd again thickened and many children swarmed all over the orange grove calling loudly. None actually came up to her but it was obvious that she was the focus of attention. She really could hardly bear it – she who had come here to escape. She was seriously thinking of leaving the place and camping up on the bare mountain even if there was no water there, when the woman came out of the house calling her imperatively. Unwillingly she rose and entered the back door to find herself in a huge kitchen. The table was heavily laden and covered with a beautiful lace cloth – she learned later that the woman's grandmother had made it and that it was only used on very special occasions. The crockery was garishly decorated with gilt and ladies in crinolines. The cutlery on the other hand was tin and tarnished. The doctor wondered at this medley of real art and sad lack of taste. When had the Greeks, even the peasants, lost their feeling for what was true?

On the table there was a brave array of food – meat, cheese, olives, bread, salad and a carafe of wine. Nikos told her proudly that his wife, Amalia, had baked the bread and he had made the wine in his own wine-press from his own grapes.

Amalia told her to sit down at the table. This she did while the five children still stood, awe-struck. Amalia herself also stood and it was obvious that they were waiting. She felt foolish sitting alone at the loaded table. The man, the father, came in and only then did they all sit. The man crossed himself. The woman and the children crossed themselves. They all murmured: 'Welcome', to which the doctor remembered the conventional reply: 'You are well found'. The children immediately reached for food.

'Eat,' the man addressed her imperiously. She ate.

She sat. She drank. And still they pressed food and wine on her.

Amalia patted her large belly. Nikos laughed loudly and said, 'Six'. The doctor had thought the woman merely fat, but now she understood that a sixth child was imminent. She felt it was really too bad, this irresponsible getting of children in poverty. Amalia then patted the doctor's flat stomach and shook her head. The doctor controlled herself not to cringe from this all-too-human contact.

Nikos said, 'You must marry first and make children afterwards.' The whole family – even the youngest – laughed tremendously. The doctor had to pretend to join in the mirth. After all they had fed her. And suddenly she found that her laughter was genuine, for she had drunk deeply and was surprised to realise that she really liked these people, needed them as if she had always known that she had missed them.

There no longer seemed any urgency to leave the friendly kitchen, but she was very tired. As she left at last, Nikos said to her, 'Tomorrow I will find fresh fish for you.'

She thanked him and walked out into the now dark orange grove. The sun had left a thin red trail in the western sky, and over to the east a full, hot moon was rising, giving form to the fantastic mountain shapes of the inland range. The cicadas sang. The village beyond was dark and quiet. Though it was, by those other standards which she had now forgotten, early, the feeling was that everyone was indoors preparing for sleep. 'How beautiful,' she thought. 'If only the whole world was like this – peaceful.' But knew in the very moment of the thought that this village world, outside the anguish of time, with its strange dominations and priorities, was not for her.

But shame in herself and in her kind of life, useful though it superficially was, lingered as she thought of the vast woman, that Mother Earth with the calm eyes and the gentle smile.

The next morning, being very tired and having overeaten and overdrunk the previous evening, she rose late. Now she had no audience outside her tent, for this was the time of work. So she prepared and ate her breakfast with a wonderful sense of peace. She then decided to wash some of her travel-stained clothes in water drawn from the well. There was a soothing unreality about herself, a not unpleasant detachment from both past and present, even future, as she slowly drew the bucket up, standing among the dark green trees. They were in blossom now and she was dizzy with the heavy scent. She pottered about a bit longer and when she caught sight of Amalia, all abustle with the morning's work, she called a natural, unreserved greeting. So it was very late, almost noon, when at last she was ready to take the path through the village and down to the sea for her first bathe.

With a few powerful strokes she reached the boat. Dead bodies were all round her, lying just below the surface of the water as if held there, trapped. But a few were still alive and struggling. However quickly she swam to and from the shore, she knew it would be impossible to save all the living, for by the time she carried one back to the land, another would have drowned. Her only course was to save the most alive by draping them over the hull of the boat where the fisherman lay. He must be all right. Why didn't he lend a hand? Surely he must be able to swim? Two could save twice as many. She shouted up at him and he raised his sick, white face as though coming out of a deep sleep. She indicated with words and gestures that he should help her hand up the girls. So commanding was her tone that he came out of shock and obeyed her, although her actual words had passed through his hearing without comprehension.

But whom should she choose to be saved? There were five or six little girls around her, all of them ready to let go of life. She had once had to choose between saving the life of a mother or her baby. It was a cruel thing. Now she could only act blindly like the hand of God. There was no time to weigh and no means of knowing. She tried to pull the nearest girl out of the water, but with no result. She dived to get a better grip. Below the surface she opened her eyes and saw with horror that thick fishing nets were floating everywhere, moving with the movement of the water, wrapping and trapping many, many bodies, drifting quiet now within the shroud with open eyes and streaming hair.

She worked quickly freeing those who had only been caught by their feet and were thus more likely to have taken air at the surface. At last she managed to pick up the first child freely, not knowing whether she was alive or dead. She raised the body up to the fisherman who grabbed the child's arm and hauled her up, landing her like a lifeless fish across the hull beside him. This she and he did again and again. Another and another. She lost count of time and numbers and life and death.

Someone was helping her now. More than one. Several. She heard their thrashing in the water beside her. She had exhausted the supply of bodies that might be alive on this side of the boat. She circled round to the other side to see if there were any there with signs of life. But only dead drowned eyes in young faces stared up at her, or rolled slowly with the sea's motion as though they were still dancing, very, very tired. And the thick dark nets swayed under and over and round them.

The priest, meanwhile, had tottered back with the surge of the crowd towards the sea. As he strove to hurry – though he could not be of any practical use – he muttered continuously in his old man's voice, 'I told them. I told them. I shouted. But they didn't hear. I waved but they didn't see. I told them the boat was unsafe. I knew the children would drown. God in your mercy, why . . .?' And so he stumbled at last on to the sad sands and drew near to the prone bodies that the men of the village had carried out of the sea. Tears ran down his time-creased cheeks and into his white beard. He was able, if nothing else, to say the prayers for the dead, to take his place of duty among the stricken crowd, to weep with them at this fearful act.

And so he came to the shore again and as of habit began to intone the prayers . . . 'In the name of the Father . . .' And as of habit all the people gathered there crossed themselves and cried, crossed themselves and perhaps some even prayed.

But as he repeated the old, old words, the words of his way of life, words that had stood, a rock through the centuries of slaughter and plague, into the priest's head or heart came a terrible doubt: 'God! Why did you let it happen?' And in a moment of pure terror he knew at last that events, good or merciless, simply happen: there is no mover, so no appeal, no comfort in this pitiful, perishable world.

The old priest wept. He had lost God and was lost.

Nikos was one of the most able-bodied men left in the village, for most of the others had left to go to a wider world and a better chance. He had been working on his farm, cutting at the winter stubble, when he heard the hubbub. At first he took little notice, knowing already that a party of school-children had come for the day. But then Amalia came out of the house more hurriedly than was fit for her bulk. Her eyes were wide with horror.

'Quick. The children in the boat,' she shouted to him.

For a second he was confused. His own children? They were all too young for such an undertaking, surely? Except the eldest – he was a nine-year-old devil. They had to be constantly on their guard, ready to pluck him from disaster. Could he have persuaded his brothers and sisters?

He ran towards the house, and as he ran he shouted, 'What children?'

'The girls. The little girls.' In spite of a swift relief, he did not break his stride, but turned down the path, shouting to other men on his way to the sea. But the path was already crowded with the ineffectual: panic-stricken women who could not swim for none of them had ever been in the water; old men who could only dodder; young children who sensed a horror and so stood around in the path impeding the progress of the swift and active ones.

At last Nikos and the others with him got free of the tangle of women and children and the aged. They burst on to the beach. Nikos was the first, sprinting across the yielding sand. He saw the boat and the girls, the woman who had shared his table in their midst, so close to land and yet so far. He dived into the water and as he came up to the shadow of the boat, he saw just under the gentle swell, the trapped bodies of the little girls. He dived, the knife from his work still in his hand, and deep down, dark in the deeper water, were more children, their hair flowing out prettily like sea-green mermaids, so beautiful were they. Only their eyes were dead. Nikos fought his way clear of the nets and the bodies, ready now, beside the woman, to cut and pull and pluck the children from the sea and sling them on to the boat.

She was aware of further commotion in the water. Men were swimming out to the boat. Many men, thank God. One by one she picked the little bodies off the boat and handed them into strong arms. Then when all the bodies had been carried off, she swam swiftly to the shore. She did not worry about the fisherman who had again, asprawl the hull, lapsed into torpor.

On the hot sand, with the help of the men, she turned the nine children thus brought back to land, on to their stomachs. Picking one at random – again to be random rather than to choose was mercifully the only course – she began artifical respiration. For a moment the men watched her, then seeing the idea, they began to imitate her on the other bodies as she gave them the slow count that just might awaken a flicker of breath in them. So shocked were the men, so urgent were the passing seconds, that not one had paused to wonder at a woman with such strength and skill. The other girls who had not been on the fatal fourth trip, the teachers, the village women and children, the priest, gathered round while she worked for over an hour first on one and then on another body.

She brought three girls back to life.

Meanwhile the other men who were not needed to help the doctor, had gone with knives into the sea to cut the other children free. One by one they brought them back and laid them in a long line on the ground. The old priest renewed his prayers, silencing the blackness in his soul. The women wailed and covered their faces. The girls cried or were silent. The teachers stood like statues oblivious of every sensation: unfeeling; dead. There was no life-flow through numbness, even in Helen Mavrou whose daughter . . .

The doctor, helped by one or two men, gently laid the three living girls under the shade of the trees.

The fisherman, it was noted by his father who had now hobbled to the scene, had disappeared.

And still they brought back the bodies and laid them on the sand. Twenty-one little girls lay wet and dead.

Now the nets lay round the boat cut and broken, the children trapped in them free, but too late for their freedom.

'Why did my son go out with the nets still on the deck?' mumbled the old man, his father. 'Why did he do this thing?' But he knew that he too had often taken the boat out with the nets still drying in the sun. It might have been himself or another man, or any man, who had set the trap and caught the victims unawares.

'He is a good boy,' he said more loudly, as though the village had already accused his son. 'He is not to blame.'

The doctor, at last knowing that nothing more could be done, spoke quietly to a few of the more likely women about sweet tea and blankets. She then left the shore, unnoticed amid the wailing and the fruitless comments, the grief and the prayers. She fled back to the village, now so very quiet and empty in the afternoon sun, back to the house that had sheltered her. Without any thought for reason or result, for Nikos' right to kindness, but only because precisely at that moment she had to, she put some money under a stone by the back door. Then having committed this act, she flung everything into her car and drove off before anyone could question her and intrude on her their own and terrible sorrow.

Amalia knew none of this nor of the true dimension when she finally, puffing, arrived on the spot with her own dear, safe children. Now she saw and heard. She said to the old fisherman, 'Why has your son disappeared, my friend?'

The old man shook his head with the scanty hair, sweat-flattened, and said, 'He is not to blame. Nobody is to blame.' Then raising his voice so that all could hear, clear above the chanting of his old enemy and friend, the priest, he cried, 'It was an accident, do you hear? The nets were there and the children were caught. That's all.'

Petrakis, Peter Vlassis and Margaret each heard the word 'blame' and their minds, each in one way or another, began tentatively to explore back on what had or had not been done; what had been said or even elusively thought. They began to waken to the terror that would soon come from other faces and eyes, from lips asking questions.

But not so Helen Mavrou. She had first stood alienated from herself, aslant, when the babble of terror-stricken girls had broken through to her outside the taverna in the village. A tingling numbness raced over her, wrapping her inwards and outwards, so that she merely followed because the others led. She was aware of stony hardness under her feet – how they hurt still! Why did they hurt? – soon to be replaced by sinking sand through which it was extremely difficult to wade. She seemed to remember having walked through this hindering softness at some other time, a long time ago. She knew now that there was some urgency forcing her to make the effort as her feet ploughed in and out, up and down, yet seemed to make no progress to wherever it was she was going.

She also felt the pressure on her arm and even recognised that the pressure was on the silk of her hot dress. She was very clear about the minute rustling noise of the material. She heard a female voice saying, 'She'll be all right, I'm sure.' But she had not the remotest idea who spoke or to whom the speaker was referring.

Then she was standing by the edge of the sea under trees. She remembered thinking that there was no sea in her usual daily life. But just to be motionless and in the shade was an enormous relief and she almost turned her head to see where she could sit down, but her self gave such a sickening lurch sideways again and the tingling sensation became so bad that she dared not make another movement, but stayed quite still clinging to herself.

She looked down at the sand and her eye caught

five or six little girls lying face downwards. That tall, fair person she vaguely remembered having seen somewhere before, was bending over one of them. There were some unknown men too bending over the other children – no, not exactly bending, but straddling them and moving rhythmically up and down while they pressed and relaxed their hold. 'Whatever are they doing? I must scold them. This is not a nice way to play. Is it perhaps some new game? I don't like it. Yes, someone had said, "They're only playing". When was that? Why must I scold them? This is something I must do. Now why? I'm a . . . I'm a . . . and these are . . .' But the thought would not come, was blocked. She worried and worried at it while the tingling shock rode her again.

Now many men were in the sea and they carried in their arms many little girls. They laid them down on the sand face upwards. Why? All the other children – there were so many of them – had also now been turned face upwards to stare into the sun. Why? And not one of them was wearing a hat . . . a hat. Pain slammed into her.

Only three little girls were lying face downwards under the trees. Now *they* were being more sensible. She must go and tell the others.

She had then a brief moment of appalling clarity – the last she would have until long after the trial, long after the world had stopped throwing questions and opinions around. Her legs moved again and she walked up and down the rows of sleeping children and each child had the face of her daughter. When she reached the first child she had recognised at once the thin, white face, the short brown hair. She had made to bend down with a fluttering cry, but some-one had held her back and said, 'No, no'.

So now she did not bend over each body, but walked up and down, up and down in the heat, passing and passing the silent rows, sometimes brushing away hands that tried to stop her, some-times hearing voices but feeling no compulsion to reply. There was no reason why they should be talking to her. And each child was her child and no child was her child. So she walked and walked until she keeled over and someone laid her under the trees with the three survivors.

Soldiers arrived with lorries. The villagers tenderly placed the dead girls on the lorries. They brought flowers, all the wild flowers of spring, and strewed the bodies with these and with the white petals of roses. The little girls were the brides they would never be. They were being given the highest honour. As brides, too, they would be buried the next day in the town. Lace and embroidery, muslin and silk. Orange blossom. So beautiful. One or two of their sad school-friends felt a strange, sour wrath.

But now the lorries with the dead, the buses with the living, and an ambulance approached the town over which the mountains had already thrown the night. The central square was a black mass of people. Silent. At the point where the cavalcade would stop stood the nomarch, the mayor, the chief of police, the army commandant, the bishop, and the head-master waiting for his wife and child.

The first bus arrived in the square. The girls who climbed out of it became each the centre of a whirl-pool. Each was seized by her parents, relatives, neighbours, brothers, sisters, grandparents. She was clutched and clung to as if her existence could not be believed. She was swallowed and sucked down with kisses and hugs; she was washed with tears of joy. She herself would cry, trying in a mother's arms, the old safe smell and texture, to blot out the sight she had seen on the shore. One fainted; another was sick.

Beyond the tight circle round each girl there was an equally insistent whirlpool of other parents, whose children, living or dead, had not arrived on the first bus. They fought to hear a name, the only name for each that mattered. There were still two more buses to arrive and the names of the dead had not yet been made known.

'Where is Lena?' 'Did you see her?' 'Was Jane on your bus?' 'Was she on the boat that overturned?' 'Will she be on the next bus?' 'Tell me. You must know.' 'Were you on the boat?' 'Who are the three living ones?'

And the children could not answer because they did not know. At last they and their parents managed to fight their way out of the square, followed home by glances almost of hatred, certainly of fear, from the other parents who must still wait for their children.

The other buses came and whenever one of the three teachers was seen to emerge, a silence fell on the crowd. Instead of gathering round, they fell apart, making way. They watched as each was led to a waiting car. And only when it had driven off, they whispered: 'Where is she going?' 'Where will they take him?' 'To prison?' 'To hospital?' 'Home?' They felt neither sympathy nor enmity. The police force that was out in strength in the square had no riot to prevent. Only as the cars drove away a murmur rose and a question passed from mouth to mouth: 'And the other teacher, the headmaster's wife, where is she?'

The little old woman, who was not old but work had made her so, had heard of the tragedy late, for she had been bent over her sewing-machine. Through the noise of the treadle, she had only gradually become aware of running and shouting in the street outside. Finally, she got up and opened the window, trying to focus her strained eyes. But by then the street was empty. The houses all round were empty. No noise and no lights. She had never known a time when there was not some neighbour to answer her call. Now there was nobody to ask, nobody at all. This in itself was so extraordinary that a feeling of great unease filled her. She went out of the room to the hall. Quite contrary to habit, she left the sewing-machine uncovered, to gather dust. She took her old, black and only coat down from its peg, patted her thin grey hair – there was no mirror – and, faltering down the rickety outside stairs in the dark, let herself out of the iron gate and so into the street. Her instinct was to make for the main square. She felt very alone and unsupported as she walked through the silent streets. Her husband had gone out with friends for an evening drink. Her elder daughter, who had left the husband chosen for her, she had left sleeping at home after an exhausting day, not made easier by the fretful infant. The baby always seemed to be quieter and more content when the younger daughter, Vasiliki, was looking after it. The old woman sighed and wondered what she was doing out on the unaccustomed streets. She was still wearing her slippers.

She found the whole town assembled in the square. She had never known it to be so crowded even on Easter Day, when even she did not work. But the crowd was not noisy and jolly. It was quiet. At that moment the third and last bus arrived, the almost last hope of those still waiting.

She did not know what had happened. She did not ask. She watched the silent girls as they descended from the bus. She watched the people. She watched as the crowd began, as before, to mill round the girls. She watched the police ready to restrain them, for the anguish had mounted as each bus arrived. She realised that the school excursion was returning. Yet how strangely! She stood there all alone, tiny and tired, and when the last girl got off the last bus, the last hope, she understood at last what all the people knew. She threw back her head and shrieked in her

92

high, cracked voice: 'My daughter? Where is my daughter?'

The crowd, whose murmur had risen to a crescendo as the last girls appeared, were silenced by the cry. Those immediately round her tried to draw away. She raised a bird-like clawed fist to the nearest figure, conscious only of its being, not of its identity. 'Where is she?' Receiving no reply, she turned and seized a man by the lapel of his jacket. 'Tell me where she is.' Her shriek was audible in all the square. Even the small circles of noise and movement round the returned girls, ceased. The town held its breath. The woman sank to her knees. 'Where is she?' She rocked back and forth, she pulled her hair over her face, she tore at it and at herself. Her scream gradually sank to a low monotonous moan as she rocked and rocked. 'My daughter, my daughter. It's time she was home. Vasiliki, come home, love, come home.'

The moan was caught up and carried from mouth to mouth, a blocked torrent that had suddenly found a vent, through the square and through the streets of the town, into the silent houses and up to the church on the hill, was taken, so it seemed, by the stars and flung into space to be lost for ever in the horror of eternity. Such things had often been, would be again, and were nothing.

So frightful was her grief, so imprisoning – like a wall over which her would-be rescuers were too tired and weak to climb, too small – that nobody could tell her that the crowd still waited for the last and most terrible return: soon a cortège would arrive

– two open lorries with the bodies and an ambulance with the survivors. Who were the dead and who were the living? Hope still flayed the parents whose children had not come. But they did not think to tell the poor woman, or perhaps they thought the chance of her daughter's survival so slim that it would be cruel to share their hope with her.

Those who had gone home with their living children, had closed and barred their doors to be able to exult and smile, cry and comfort in privacy; to feed and then tuck into bed the shocked infants that had come back to them, souls spared by a merciful God. 'Tomorrow we shall light a candle.' 'I will make a pilgrimage barefoot to the monastery of St Catherine.' 'I shall donate a thousand drachmas to the church.' Each according to his or her means, felt the need to pay God for saving a child, to bribe, maybe, for future mercy.

The rest waited. Those who were not directly concerned spoke together in low voices, telling over names. They spoke of the children and their families. They spoke of the officials waiting rigid by the road-side, now joined by doctors and nurses. They commented on the fact that the mayor's daughter had not gone on the excursion because she had been ill. They spoke about one of the doctors standing there ready to help. His daughter had not returned. They spoke of the teachers. The 'French' girl had hidden her face when she got out of the bus. She had practically run to the waiting police car as if prison was a freedom from the people who stared. The mathematics teacher – some knew his name, some did not – had, on the other hand, walked through the crowd almost . . . boldly. The religion man, what was his name? Petrakis, had not been spotted by most. Nor was his wife to be seen anywhere in the crowd. Was she at home? Had she gone to meet him? Had she left town? The uninvolved speculated. Or if they did not speak but just stayed there on and on, it was because they were magnetised by disaster, a break in routine, the smell of death.

But mostly they waited and were wordless. The commotion caused by the little woman had ceased; even the birds no longer twittered and fought in the old elm trees; no bell tolled, for the order had not yet been given. Then at last the first lorry came to a halt at the point where the leaders of the town were standing, cordoned off by a chain of police. Those who were standing at a certain height on door-steps or balconies, could see that ten children lay inside. They lay prim and neat, their wet skirts smoothed down, the sand washed from eyes and mouths, their bodies strewn with flowers. In the second lorry there were eleven.

The nurses came forward with stretchers and one by one, in total silence, under the light of the old street lamps, the children were carried off to the church. But first the sad procession passed the chiefs, who stood with heads bowed, hatless. And as they passed, the headmaster made identification. In a voice loud and firm, as though he had steeled himself to this last forlorn duty of his public service, he called each name. And as each name was heard, a small group of parents detached themselves from the crowd, passed through the cordon and accompanied the stretcher up to the church. Only Penny's mother was not there and she had to wait for her father to finish. He had not hesitated when he called her name.

At last with all the names called, there remained three families who had not seen their children either living or dead. Almost shyly they approached the ambulance as if their tremendous joy was a thing to be hidden in shame, or a thing so fragile that merely to think might break it. The three children were brought out on stretchers, wrapped in blankets, and their parents looked upon their living, sleeping faces. Helen Mavrou stayed sitting rigid in the ambulance. Her husband gently called her name, but she did not hear him in the place where she had fled. The children, once acknowledged by their parents, were replaced and the ambulance left the square for the hospital. In silence, the parents followed, not daring to tempt man or God with their happiness.

3   The Village

'Did he drown?' asked one; the other said:
'He drowned.' The third one looked at them
helpless from the bottom of the sea, the way
one looks at drowned people.
        Yannis Ritsos: 'The Third One' 1969

The days passed. This truism has a particular truth of its own when one day seems to refuse to let the other days come, pulls each day back stickily into itself, so that finally you wonder if ever there will be a large enough space of time between you and that day. The town, after the funeral, gathered itself more closely within its mountain barrier, resented the strangers who came to ask questions. They were relieved that the trial of the teachers and the fisherman would take place in another town innocent of passion.

The questions and the trials went on and on until it seemed that the whole country was on trial. And it was all about a few little words like 'freedom', 'responsibility', 'guilt'. These had been words that people had hidden at the back of their minds, just as they hid forbidden records or books at the back of a cupboard, covering them with old clothes. But suddenly the words had to be freed of dust and used again, their essence debated anew in a new light. People began to shake themselves out of the torpor or coma, began to realise what they were in danger of becoming – for the true horror of dictatorship lies not in the dramatic cruelties but in the daily erosion of the individual will to make decisions and accept responsibility. So, in some strange way, the tragedy of the schoolgirls was the beginning of the end. The doctor, untraced by the police and back now in her busy hospital routine, remarked to one whom she trusted in the secret nights when flitting figures came and went on their exile road to freedom: It was like the *Titanic*, she said. Suddenly everything was changed, an epoch ended and began.

But all this was much later.

In the village, the terrible event had dragged the villagers down to the sea, had made men leave their fields and animals untended, women leave their pots aboil and the washing unrinsed. The old had hobbled and the young had run. Each had shouted advice that was unheard and untaken. But in the event, the young and youngish men who were still living in the dying village and who could swim had proved swift and effective. Of that, at least, the village could be proud. But for many days afterwards, the village was synonymous with tragedy: the villagers would open their newspapers to read headlines all screaming the name of their own home. 'Do you want another . . .?' 'What can we do to prevent another . . .?' And more dangerously: 'Who is responsible for . . .?'

In varying degrees the village, the town, the country mourned the death of the little girls. The nearer one was, the more acutely. Schoolgirls in the capital, for example, were truly shocked, felt the hair rising on their arms, obeyed their parents for a few days and then forgot. A few of them began to question, just as a few had questioned the bridal beauty of the funeral in the town. But for most people not of that immediate area, it was: 'How terrible! Did you read that?' 'Twenty-one little girls drowned! How can people be so careless!' Then they started their housework or went to their offices. They, after all, had no responsibility.

The village had been closest of all. They had offered help where they could: a bowl of water, a chair. In the last analysis, it was not their children who lay on the sand with eyes open to the sun, but they soon realised, just as the people of the town had, that they would never be quite the same again. That night many a mother in the village clutched her own child more tightly, spoke more gently, felt how unpredictable was the arrival of Charon. Perhaps they did not reach the priest's terrible conclusion, for though fatalistic in their religion, they still believed, more vehemently now through fear, that their favourite saints could be bribed and wooed.

The villagers had watched sadly with a sigh and a muttered prayer as the three buses with the living had departed from the square. They had watched the arrival of two army lorries and an ambulance, which had been sent after a telephone call to the town. That call was later strongly criticised for it had been hurried and garbled. No attempt had been made to give names, thus causing unnecessary anguish among the parents waiting in the town. Some villagers asked the woman at the coffee-shop who it was that had made the call. Only she would know, for there was no other telephone in the village. But she did not know. She was too confused. So it remained just another mystery.

Worst of all, they had watched the procession of men each carrying a limp blue girl, coming up the path from the sea. They had watched the children carefully laid out on the floor of the lorries. Some housewives had offered to sweep them first so that the children should not get dirty, but the lorry drivers had said brusquely – even they, young conscripts, were deeply moved – that it was not necessary and there was no time. 'No time for what?' the villagers wondered.

Some of the women had thrown flowers on to them. Even the men had been unashamed of tears.

The three little girls who had been saved had been put in one of the village houses. Gently they had been laid on beds and covered with blankets against shock. The village women clucked and fussed round them with basins to be sick in, with sweet tea, with towels. The three children had gazed at them unblinking as if they were something other than simple human beings. One woman said, 'It gave me the creeps it did. The way they stared. As if *we* were dead and drowned.'

Soon after the lorries, the ambulance had arrived with two nurses from the town hospital. The little girls were given sedatives, kissed enormously by the women, put on stretchers and taken to the ambulance followed by a huge crowd. Almost unnoticed Helen Mavrou was carried out of another house and put in the same ambulance. And so at last they had all gone, gone away from the village, away from the sea they had so eagerly welcomed in the morning; but never away from the nightmare. In the early evening twilight, the lights of the vehicles could be seen for a long time winding up the mountain road behind the village. The people stayed all together in the square until nothing more was there.

Then, and only then, did they begin to look about them at the familiar places and faces, shake themselves, and realise that they were still themselves. Then only did they remember animals abandoned and bleating to be milked, water undrawn, vegetables parched. Then only did they remember what their thoughts had been before and what their problems would be tomorrow.

Slowly, almost regretfully, they each turned inwards to their own lives, the women still tut-tutting with their tongues. Nikos and his wife came back to their house to find that the strange woman had gone. She had left some money under a stone by the back door. Nikos was quite bewildered with hurt when he saw it, and sullenly refused to make any comment, even to his wife. The woman had left no note, so nothing was ever known about her . . . not even her name. A child found a packet of sandwiches by the roadside, opened it and ate them. The old fisherman went home and found the two women – his wife and his daughter – in tears. The boy had not yet returned.

All went about their business, but half-heartedly. Even the tiny ones who were not yet articulate knew that this had been a day like no other day, and when they were much older they would embroider the tale as if they too had played a major part in it. One little boy who was not yet five years old at the time, would tell his own son, 'I jumped into that rough sea, waves as high as a man, and swam out to the wreck. I took a girl out of the water and swam with her to the shore. I saved her life.' And the child, who loved a story, would ask for the details again and again. But that was far in the future. Now it was too early for myths.

The villagers, men, women and children, having attended to what was absolutely necessary, as if by common instinct, wandered back to the square. Never had the coffee-shop owner had so many customers. All the village was there. Nobody commented on the presence of the women in that essentially male domain. The children, tired but excited, crawled round and under chairs and tables and feet, whined for water or listened to the incomprehensible voices. The owner's wife begged chairs from neighbours to accommodate the crowd. The tiny shop itself was full and bursting, so that most of the villagers had to sit outside overflowing into the roadway. The night was chilly, but nothing would persuade them home.

They spoke about the day in soft voices with only an occasional rise of anger. Especially they spoke about the parents of the dead. But this sad chorus was interrupted by some of the men who wanted to settle certain practical matters: the schoolmaster declared that tomorrow, the day of the funeral, he would close the school as a sign of mourning and the national flag in the school yard would be at half-mast. In fact, he quite surprised himself at his daring in thus taking the initiative, making a decision for himself without waiting for an order from above. Normally, each word he spoke in school to his children was ordered to be this and only this, most certainly not that. The same of course for books. Even excursions were the result of an official document from 'them'. It really made him wonder, and he felt pleased with the gesture that he, all by himself, was making. Sensing, among some of the other men, a slight frisson at his daring, he continued firmly, 'If we listen to the radio tonight, we may even hear a general order to that effect. In any case, I plan to assemble the whole school tomorrow morning and deliver to them a funeral oration.' He sat down emphatically.

The priest now declared his intention of saying mass for the dead in the village church and discussed the relative timetables with the schoolmaster so that the two ceremonies would not overlap. In contrast to the schoolmaster, the old priest, not being a civil servant, felt no fear. In truth he hardly knew anything about the government of his country. Mind you, he had heard tell of a priest in another village who had been arrested because they had found some book or other in his house. That did seem a bit high-handed, but that is what 'they' were like. He himself had no books and now that the one power he recognised had gone, nothing mattered any more. The mass was just a gesture for his flock. Though he himself had been abandoned, he would never abandon them or shatter their simple faith.

Finally the village doctor rode into the square on his horse. He had only just heard the news as he had been up in the mountain villages all day attending to two women in childbirth. He very much regretted his absence. 'I could have helped with resuscitation and perhaps saved more lives,' he said. 'But how was I to know?'

A man was heard to mutter that 'they' should send more doctors, one for every village. Those who heard looked askance and pretended not to hear.

Having disposed of these matters, they all continued to retrace the day's events, each telling his or her story, contradicting and asserting. It was not long, therefore, before someone said, 'Who was that "foreign" woman who saved the three little girls?' Most of them had not, at the time, made an immediate connection between the sloppy 'hippy' who had so amused them last night when she camped in the orange grove behind Nikos' house, and the efficient woman who had swum and rescued, who had organised them, the men, to save lives. And who then had vanished. It was that, seeing her manner of life and dress, they had all formed certain preconceived ideas about her, ideas so rooted in prejudice that they could not easily adjust to another set of circumstances. The villagers, in any case, had been wholly occupied with the girls and everything had been so confused – now there were hardly two opinions alike on what had happened – that they had only noted that the 'foreign' woman was there and helping. Now they had time to think and question.

Nikos said, 'She is a woman – from the north I think – who camped on my land last night.'

'Where is she now? We must go and thank her.' There was a general murmur of assent.

The village doctor, to show he bore no ill-will at the woman's usurpation of his trade, said loudly, 'Indeed, yes. It was a remarkable performance for an untrained woman. I can't understand how . . .'

But Nikos interrupted him. 'She's gone,' he said.

'Gone?' The villagers looked at each other aware that they had seriously failed in a social obligation. Some of them remembered having stared at her last night, others remembered having seen her walk down to the beach at noon. And they had tittered. But none had seen her go.

'How do you know she's gone?' asked someone hopefully.

Nikos would never, never mention the insulting

money, so he said, 'When I went back home an hour ago, there wasn't a sign of her tent or her things. Besides her car has gone.' It was irrefutable.

'And she knew how to swim!'

'It was a miracle the way she saved those three girls.'

'She was sent by God.'

'And a woman too. How extraordinary!'

The doctor cut through the voices. 'It was no miracle. She certainly knew how to give artificial respiration. I've said time and again that these are skills, like swimming, that should be taught in every school, instead of wasting children's time on useless . . .' Like the schoolmaster, the doctor found his words blocked by a current of fear in his audience. It was years since there had been such an assembly in the village. The men had almost forgotten what it was to speak of things openly, knowing that those who always informed were, as now, listening.

The women had never spoken, but now it was they more particularly who would have none of this scientific talk. The idea took root and grew that a miracle had been performed and that the strange woman from nowhere had been sent by God. The priest remained silent.

Into the middle of this fascinating conversation a jeep screeched. All eyes turned to it as it raced round the square importantly and jerked to a halt outside the coffee-shop. It was white and some who had seen such things in town, recognised that it was a police car.

An officer of police jumped out smartly and saluted the crowd in general. 'Who is in charge here?' he asked.

The villagers looked at each other in confusion. They were not used to the police. The occasional case of 'village' crime such as an injury in a vendetta or incest, were on the whole settled by the villagers themselves. They resented outside authority and were strangers to the more 'civilised' crimes of theft and murder. Besides, they were not at all sure who exactly *was* in charge, never having need of such a category of person. However, some of the men knew that, in accordance with the law, each village must have a president. Some of them even vaguely remembered who he was, though any real local authority had for many years been usurped by the capital.

The president himself suddenly recollected his position. It was Uncle Stathis, the taverna owner. He came forward. The police officer saluted again and asked the old man to tell him what he knew. But Uncle Stathis being old had been among the last to arrive on the beach. He had been a witness only as the last bodies were being brought out of the sea. He did however speak of the four teachers who had lunched at his taverna while the girls had still been out at sea in the boat. He spoke only of the facts. He did not criticise. But of course his evidence was the most damning of all.

'They are under arrest,' said the officer. The village gasped. 'But I have come about another matter. Where is the old fisherman?'

He had been sitting well in the background, thankful that all the talk had so far been about the foreign woman. Now he was obliged to indicate his presence.

'What do you want with me?'

'Old man,' said the officer, 'where is your son?'

'I . . . he's somewhere around, I suppose,' he mumbled.

'Go and find him and bring him here at once.'

Again the village gasped. Could it be that they, after all, were also involved in the guilt?

The old man shuffled off towards his tiny two-roomed cottage at the seaward end of the village. He had no idea where his son was, though the weeping of his women-folk had made him uneasy. He had no very clear opinion of what part his son had or had not played in the tragedy, apart from the fact that he had been in charge of the boat. After his one unguarded outburst there on the shore, he had made himself forget about the nets carelessly left dangling. It was also a measure of the shock the village had received that during that evening assembly at the coffee-shop no accusation had been made. All the village knew about the nets but had not connected them intimately with the tragedy, perhaps because they did not want to.

The old man had himself, coming late among the aged, glimpsed what he took to be his son lying inert athwart the upturned hull. Then he had not been there. He remembered commenting on this – or had Amalia said something? The foreign woman might have seen him but they said she had gone. The young men who had swum out to the boat might have seen him, but they were too busy recounting what they had seen in the water, each one fitting his tale to his personality, to have bothered about the familiar figure of the boy. They had known him for nineteen years so he held no interest, and besides, they were sure he was not dead.

It seemed natural for the old man, obeying the police officer's order, to go home, though he knew the boy was not there. When he arrived, the house was dark and cold with the unprecedented absence of the two women. Having wept, they had both decided to go to the coffee-shop with the rest of the village. There at least they would have companionship and perhaps the boy would turn up there, drawn by the talk and the lights. When the officer had ordered him to find his son, his wife had, it was true, offered to come home with him and help. But the old man felt that he must be alone. His wife, and more especially his daughter, had been relieved by this refusal. The coffee-shop was a rare novelty. Besides, the boy was often absent for hours following his own lonely course in and around the village. He was not a child in the sense of having to be watched. It was only the policeman who had implied that he was missing.

So he went into the dark house alone. Because he

could as yet think of no practical course of action, he dragged an upright chair from the kitchen and set it outside the front door. He sat down. There was nothing to see save the half-imagined shapes of familiar bushes, and the blacker rectangle of a house further up the road. No lights. The whole village was up there in the square. There was no moon, for in its full phase it rose early, leaving the greater part of the night in darkness. The village path could not boast of street lamps. The old man lifted his head and sighed. The stars were bright and near.

It was good to be quiet for a moment. He must try to make up his mind whether he should be worried or not. He supposed it must be about eleven o'clock. Usually the whole village would have been asleep at this time. The boy was always home by now, for what else could he do, where else could he go? In the village, to have a girlfriend was out of the question.

He scratched his head and sighed again. He was surprised to hear footsteps crunching towards his house along the rough, dark path. The salt of the sea came to him coolly on the air. He shivered. Would it be his son? But the steps did not lift and spring; they dragged and shuffled. Then, as the figure cleared the thicker trees so that he was outlined against open space, he recognised, from the tall hat, blacker against black starlight, that it was the priest. 'What the devil does he want?' he thought.

He got up quickly so that the priest would not think he had been idling instead of carrying out the policeman's orders. His chair scraped. The priest called out, 'So there you are then. Is that you?'

'Yes. What do you want?'

The priest was now coming up towards the house, groping.

'Put on a bit of light. What are you doing in the dark? I thought you might need some help.'

'What sort of help do you think you can give me, old man?'

'I hadn't thought,' replied the priest simply.

For want of something more constructive to do, the fisherman went into the kitchen, fumbled on the table for the paraffin lamp and matches. Having lit the lamp, he brought it out and hung it on the iron hook skewered into the front wall of the house.

'That's better,' said the priest. 'The boy may like to see a light in his house.'

The words struck oddly on the old fisherman. Apprehension, from being a pale ghost on the outer edge of his vision, became a black spectre within his soul. He looked at the priest in the harsh, flaring light. He looked very tired and very, very old. Or was it the light that threw the deep lines on his face into such violent contrast? But then the old fool must be really old. He himself was seventy and he remembered the priest as a big boy coming home from the seminary for the holidays when he himself was not yet through the village primary school. He suddenly felt very glad of someone at his side. One of his own kind.

The priest sat down heavily on the chair. 'Has the boy come home?' he asked, though it was obvious that he had not. When he got no reply, he said, 'Where would he likely be?' The father then made an effort to answer. 'Of an evening he would sometimes go to the coffee-shop to play tric-trac. But not tonight. Tonight there is anyway no entertainment. They'll even have turned the radio off when they've listened to the news.'

'Would he ever go for a walk alone?'

'Many a time. He liked to be alone. But never so late at night. You can't see a thing.'

'Did he maybe have a girl? Excuse me for suggesting it.'

'A girl? You know as well as I do that the few girls still left in the village are not to be got like that.'

'No, no. I suppose not. It's a pity how all the young have gone. I expect the children will go too when they grow up. There's nothing for them here. The village will die. I wonder your son never wanted to go.'

'He's a good boy.'

'Yes of course . . .' The two old men sighed together as the tiny insects of the night stirred and rustled.

'Well,' said the priest. 'I suppose we must get on.'
'Where to?'

'The sea is as good a place as any.'

The fisherman said, 'Let's have a drop of brandy before we go. You look as if you need it.'

'You're not so good yourself,' retorted the priest, with a brief memory of old antagonism.

When they had swallowed the brandy, the fisherman said, 'We'd better take the lamp.'

He unhooked it from the wall and held it high as he guided the priest's steps and his own along the path towards the soft surr-surr of the sea.

Meanwhile the police officer, whose mission it was to get what information he could from the villagers, preparatory to the public prosecuter's case to be presented in court on the day after the funeral, was questioning the other villagers at the coffee-shop. Uncle Stathis had already deposed how the four teachers had sat down to eat their lunch while the girls were still at sea in the boat. This was already known to the police and the teachers themselves had made no effort to deny it. If this fact had been made known to the public when the teachers had returned on the buses, there might have been the feared riot. As it was, it only became known after the first anguish and when people were dispersed.

The officer now wanted to know why no respons-ible person from the village had been near at the time of the tragedy. 'After all, the boy who took them out is very young. Surely someone else should have been with him?'

The villagers, feeling themselves accused, drew together against him. Amalia spoke for all in her thick, country voice: 'We could not know that the boy had agreed to take them out. He arranged it himself and told no one. And if we had known, we could not know that the children were still at sea. We heard and saw many girls in the olive grove over there, but we did not know their numbers so how could we guess that some were not . . .'

A murmur of approval greeted this logic, though most of the men and some of the women resented her thus acting as spokesman. Obscurely they felt that it was not fitting for a woman to do so. More directly, many of them disliked her because, as they thought, she set herself apart. She acted as though she was superior to them since her husband was more energetic than most and therefore richer. Who did she think she was? Furthermore, there was the old memory that her husband, Nikos, had been active in the civil war. Inevitably, some liked him and some did not. It was an old quarrel that took a long time dying. But not one of the villagers would have dreamt of letting any such hint drop to an outsider like the policeman. The whole affair merely coloured the undercurrent when Amalia had finished speaking.

So a man cut in: 'As you could see for yourself if it wasn't so dark, all our houses lie away from the sea. They say our village was built like that because of pirates. Being so far from the sea, the villagers could be warned in time of an attack. My grandmother . . .' The crowd scornfully jeered him into silence and another took up the tale.

'What he's trying to tell you is that you couldn't see the shore from the village. You have to go right down that path – it's about half a kilometre – and round the little hill with the vines to get on to the beach. It was noon so of course all of us men were working in the fields and the women were in their kitchens.'

'I see,' said the officer. 'So none of you had anything to do with the accident. None of you saw anything.'

'That's right,' said Uncle Stathis, the president, firmly.

'Except for the priest,' said someone in a low voice, but the officer did not hear him.

'Then what about the foreign woman?'

Now that the village no longer felt threatened, they were ready to open up on that subject. The fair, tall, non-sexed stranger had already been translated in their minds into an angel. She had come to the village for no apparent reason – it was not yet the tourist season – had performed her miracle, and had vanished as mysteriously into the world beyond the mountains. Having created this first myth, the villagers were ripe with the desire to impress their vision on anyone who would listen. But from the police officer's point of view, there was a surprising and irritating lack of hard facts.

'She came yesterday.' Amalia led the conversation again, not caring that her neighbours disliked her for this and other violations of the unwritten law. 'She wanted to camp on our land. My husband refused to take any money from her.' She turned her head to the murmur that arose at this – a murmur probably of disbelief. Her dignity silenced further comment. The police officer tapped his notebook with his pen impatiently. So far he had not been able to write anything.

'What was her name?'

'I don't know.'

'Does anybody know?' There was a general shaking of heads at this question. Angels do not have names.

'Where did she come from?'

'I don't know.'

'Is the land yours?'

Nikos, sensing a danger, hastened to answer for his wife. 'It's my land. I gave her permission to camp there.'

The police officer seemed to be relieved to be dealing with a man. He became severe: 'You must be aware that all strangers are required to show their identity card to the hotel or camping site or room where they are staying. And that the landlord is then required to give all this information to the police. Otherwise, how could we keep track of people?'

Nikos stuttered for a moment, wondering how to deal with the voice of authority. He had had enough trouble in the civil war – prison, torture – he did not want any more. At last he said, 'I have not got a camping site. It's only that she asked me as a favour . . .'

'No matter. The principle is the same. You have been very careless. The law must be obeyed.' The police officer, who liked the sound of what he was saying, could have gone on for a long time in this vein, but he remembered that he had still not written anything in his notebook. If he did not do something about it soon, he too would be in trouble from his superiors.

'When did she go down to the beach?'

'About noon. I don't know the exact time.' If only he could write something exact! He pressed the point.

Amalia now replied. 'We are not in the habit of consulting clocks in the village. That's for townsfolk.'

A point to the village. They silently cheered.

'Why did she go down to the beach? Did she tell you?'

'No. I suppose she wanted to swim. Foreigners do – even women.'

The police officer pounced. 'So she was a foreigner then?'

Nikos said, 'My wife only means that she was not from this area. She was from some other part of Greece. We call such people foreigners.'

'Did she take her swimming suit then?'

'No.' There was a murmur of puzzlement.

Nikos said, 'She was wearing it – under her clothes.'

Amalia said too quickly, 'How do you know?' For a brief moment there were spurts of laughter. Amalia flushed angrily.

Nikos rode the laughter. 'I don't think it's a subject for joking.' His words made them all remember the dead.

'Then?' prompted the policeman.

'Then, nothing. I didn't see her again until we were all in the water trying to get the children out.'

A young man broke in, 'I was the first of the village men down there by the shore . . .'

Interruption. 'You weren't. I was . . .'

'Sh – sh,' hissed the crowd. The first young man continued, 'I went down to the water and I saw someone hauling the children on to the hull. I dashed in and began to help. I didn't really know who it was. There wasn't time to think of anything except getting them out of the water.'

Approval. The village had brave young men.

'Did you see the fisherman's son anywhere?'

'I didn't notice.'

'You don't seem any of you to have noticed very much,' reproved the police officer. 'How do you know it was in fact the foreign woman?'

'I didn't then, but afterwards when she came out of the water, we all saw her. We recognised her from last night.'

Another man said, 'She had already lifted five bodies on to the boat. Single-handed. And a woman!'

'Then when she came out of the water she seemed to know exactly what to do.'

'She saved three children.'

The women of the village took up the chorus. 'Sent by God she was.'

'The Lord and the Blessed Virgin,' added another for good measure, crossing herself three times.

'A miracle.'

'A saint.'

The police officer cut across this canonisation.

'And you can't tell me any more? None of you?' He looked round at the faces, flickering in their various shape, line and texture in the pale lamplight from the open door of the coffee-shop. He looked into each pair of eyes, and each returned his gaze. Until at last a small boy piped, 'The fisherman's son was there. I saw him. He was lying across the boat.'

Again the point of guilt had been reached. The schoolmaster stood up abruptly. 'Well, we have much to do tomorrow. I think we should all go home now.' They all began to push back chairs, get to their feet, wander off. They did not think of asking the officer's permission, and he still fuming with an empty notebook. They all went, not wanting to be questioned further.

'One moment,' called the officer to their retreating backs. 'Where does the fisherman live? I sent him off half an hour ago to fetch his son.'

But they all hastened away, not turning back at his question. Only the doctor, who was not of the village, reluctantly paused and replied, 'Come with me. I'll show you the way'.

At last, for most, the day was over. They scattered to their houses and their neglected tasks. Children fretfully already slept in the arms of parents carrying them home. The square was empty and the borrowed chairs had disappeared. Everybody had gone home, except for the doctor and the police officer who together took the path to the fisherman's cottage.

When they arrived at the cottage, it was in darkness. They made out two figures standing in the doorway. The doctor always carried a small torch, which he now shone on to the faces of the old man's wife and daughter.

'Is your son here?'

'No!'

'Your husband?'

The woman impassively gave the same answer. The girl began to whimper behind her hand.

'Where is your husband?'

The girl broke out, 'Father's taken the lamp!'

So the two men left them there without another word. Instinctively they continued towards the sea. As they rounded the last bend and came to the point where the path ended and the soft sand began, they stood for a moment looking forwards to the dark hollow of land and sea and sky. At first it seemed quite empty, as if all life had for ever gone. But then far away at the tip of the promontory, among the trees, they thought they could discern a light. It was low down as if it had been placed on the ground. They were not sure if they could, among the stirring shadows and the shapes of the trees, see any figures near the light or not.

They hurried on.

As they came closer, approaching from the land-ward side and therefore behind the light, they could see that a figure was in fact sitting on the ground near the lamp. At his side was another. For some reason, perhaps engendered by the tensity of the two people sitting there, they went more quietly now, so that finally they were able to come up behind the trees without having been seen or heard.

The priest had taken off his hat and looked in the crude lamplight, vulnerable, as though stripped of what he was. The old fisherman was hunched up beside him. They were both talking in low voices, but were not looking at each other, but rather out to sea. One almost expected to find a third person talking to them out there.

The police officer and the doctor stayed very still behind the trees, straining to listen.

'What can we do?' said the father.

'We are too old to swim.'

'He can't swim. My son can't swim.'

'Can't swim?'

'No.'

'But he is a fisherman. He has a boat. And you tell me he can't swim.'

'That's right.'

'Then how did he get out there when he wasn't there before?'

'I don't know.'

The priest continued in his relentless, wearied voice. 'The question is how did he get away from the boat in the first place? I myself saw him on the boat before the . . . and you said he was there on the upturned hull at first and then he wasn't there.'

He sensed the father's shrug.

He scratched his bare head in puzzlement. The doctor and the officer remained still silent behind the trees wondering what would be revealed.

The father said into the darkness, 'A miracle, perhaps. God wanted my son to be saved. That is what you would say.'

Like a sigh, the old priest said, 'I do not believe . . .'

'What! You do not believe in miracles? But this is your trade.'

'In God, my old friend. In God. What God is it that let this . . . this happen?'

And from some distant, youthful catechism, half-learnt and half-forgotten, that the old priest himself may have taught him as a child, the fisherman replied, 'It is not God. But man's evil'.

'No, no, no! No man is so evil. No God is so evil. These were innocent virgins. God would have looked after his own.'

The fisherman said, 'You must believe in God, old man. You will soon die.'

'You tell me to believe in God. You . . .?'

'Yes, I. Because if *you* lose your faith, who is there to help my son?'

The old priest bent his head and was silent.

The police officer chose this moment to come forward although the doctor tried to restrain him yet. He felt that he must get on with his duty or he would be criticised for being so long and so empty-handed. Besides, he was not at all sure that he should not report this conversation. In this land, this country, everyone was obliged outwardly to accept God in the Church as part of the system.

'Have you found your son?' he asked.

'Yes.'

'Where is he?'

'Over there.' The father gestured towards the dark sea and the barely visible hulk of the boat.

'What do you mean?'

The old man replied wearily, hopelessly, 'If you raise this lamp up high so that the light falls far on the water, you will see my son lying on the boat.'

The officer did so, and both the men saw a dark figure lying spreadeagled on his stomach across the upturned hull. The figure did not move.

'Is he . . .?'

'I do not know.'

The doctor and the officer were vigorous and fairly young, so they flung off their outer clothing and plunged into the star-broken water, leaving the two old ones alone on the shore. Very soon they reached the boat and trod water beneath its steep side, looking up at the face of the boy looking down at them with unrecognising eyes.

'What is it, boy? What are you doing there?' asked the officer.

The young man answered, 'I am looking at their faces. They are singing.'

'Come home with us now,' suggested the doctor.

Surprisingly, he offered no objection and slid down into their waiting arms. When, between them, they had got him ashore, the doctor said, 'Why did you go back there?'

'That is where they were waiting for me.'

'The drowned girls?'

'I was drowned. They were looking down at me.'

The doctor thought it best to ignore this, and, as the officer was obviously out of his depth, he pursued, 'Why did you lie on the boat and watch them instead of helping them?'

'I cannot swim.'

'You could have pulled some of them up – I mean earlier, more quickly before that woman arrived and told you what to do.'

'They were not dead. They were dancing and laughing. They were singing.'

At last the officer had a question he could get to grips with. 'How did you get ashore if you cannot swim?'

'I don't know. God gave me strength to swim.'

'And now? How did you get back to the boat?'

As the boy did not answer, the officer found another question. 'Where were you hiding all after-noon when everybody was looking for you?'

'Hiding? Why should I hide? I lay under a tree. Sometimes I looked up at the birds in the sky. Some-times I slept.'

'Why did you go back to the boat?'

'I told you. They were waiting for me there.'

The two men began to put on their clothes.

The officer said, 'You'll have to come back with me to the town.'

The doctor tried to interrupt. 'He's in need of . . .'

'He'll be treated as necessary. That's not for me.'

'All right,' said the boy as if the words had no

meaning.

'Old men,' called the officer to the silent figures who had not moved. 'Go back to your homes now. The boy will be safe.'

The priest and the fisherman rose unsteadily on cramped limbs. They let the boy and his escort pass before them into the night and then they themselves turned landward walking sadly towards the village.

As the officer led the boy along the path past his home, the doctor said, 'He should change into dry clothes.' But the boy shook his head and walked on as if he had never known his home. So they brought him to the police car in the now deserted square. Only a few late villagers saw him, from behind their windows, get in, saw him being driven off, and wondered. The police officer, sitting beside the boy in the car, was satisfied at last. He had caught the victim and was no longer empty-handed.